Introduction to Organic Reaction Mechanisms

McGraw-Hill Chemistry-Biology Interface Series

Charles C. Price, Editor
Department of Chemistry, University of Pennsylvania

Editorial Board: Aubrey W. Naylor, Duke University; Robert W. Burris, University of Wisconsin; L. Carroll King, Northwestern University; Leonard K. Nash, Harvard University

Introduction to Organic Reaction Mechanisms

An Interface Book of the Advisory Council
on College Chemistry and the Commission
on Undergraduate Education in the Biological
Sciences.

Otto Theodor Benfey

Earlham College

McGraw-Hill Book Company

New York, St. Louis, San Francisco, Düsseldorf,
London, Mexico, Panama, Sydney, Toronto

Introduction to Organic Reaction Mechanisms

Library of Congress Catalog Card Number: 77–95794

1 2 3 4 5 6 7 8 9 0 BABA 7 9 8 7 6 5 4 3 2 1 0

This book was set in Times New Roman by Spottiswoode, Bal-
lantyne and Co. Ltd., and printed on permanent paper and bound
by George Banta Company, Inc. The designer was Marsha
Cohen; the drawings were done by Philip Cohen. The editors
were Jeremy Robinson and Anne Marie Horowitz. Matt Martino
supervised the production.

to my teachers

Louis P. Hammett
Sir Christopher Ingold
Frank H. Westheimer

Three guides in the field of
Physical Organic Chemistry

The Chemistry-Biology Interface Series

Several years ago, a few dozen biologists, chemists, physicists and other scientists spent several days on the campus of the University of Washington under the joint sponsorship of the Commission on Undergraduate Education in Biology, the Advisory Council on College Chemistry and the Commission on College Physics. The purpose was to study ways to improve teaching in areas of mutual concern to two or more of the disciplines involved. The group considering the area between chemistry and biology agreed that a series of paperback books, prepared for elementary college level students in either biology or chemistry, could serve a useful purpose toward this end.

Prepared by authorities in their fields, these books could, for the chemists, indicate the biological significant reactions useful to illustrate chemical principles and, for the biologist, summarize up-to-date information on molecular phenomena of significance to a modern understanding of biological systems.

To implement this proposal, CUEBS and AC$_3$ appointed an editorial committee of:

Professor Robert H. Burris, Department of Biochemistry, University of Wisconsin

Professor L. Carroll King, Department of Chemistry, Northwestern University

Professor Leonard K. Nash, Department of Chemistry, Harvard University

Professor Aubrey W. Naylor, Department of Botany, Duke University

Professor Charles C. Price, Department of Chemistry, University of Pennsylvania

to organize the undertaking.

As of this writing, the following volumes are in preparation:

Myron Bender, "Catalysis"
Melvin Calvin, "Chemical Evolution"
Roderick K. Clayton, "Light and Living Matter: Volume II"
Paul M. Doty, "Macromolecules"
David E. Greene, "Surfaces, Films, and Membranes"
Charles C. Price, "Geometry and Interactions of Molecules"

It is our hope that the material in these volumes will prove of sufficient interest to teachers and students in elementary college chemistry and biology courses that much of it will ultimately be incorporated in regular textbooks.

Charles C. Price

Philadelphia, Pennsylvania

Preface

Unchanging systems are easier to understand and describe than changing ones because we have *time* to observe the given state of the system. If the system changes, time has to be incorporated into our description of it. For instance, the mechanics of taking photographs is easier than that of filmmaking and even in filmmaking a continuously changing scene is recreated as a series of still photographs run off too rapidly to be distinguished by the eye. Historically in the sciences, the description of static phenomena preceded the description of dynamic phenomena. The laws of the balance and of the lever were worked out in classical Greece while the mathematical description of falling bodies had to await the seventeenth century and Galileo. Classical physics, whose objects do not change their nature but only their location in space and time, was put in mathematical form long before chemistry. And when chemical change did succumb to mathematical analysis, in the early nineteenth century, at first only the initial and final states were described. The *process of change,* the *mechanism* of chemical change, became an exact science many decades later.

Biology, whose objects (organisms) visibly are born, grow, mature, age, and die, was mathematized—and then only in part—even later than chemistry.

I have attempted in this book, designed for beginning students in biology or chemistry, to separate some of the factors that influence the speed of chemical reactions and the direction of chemical change, that is, the nature and quantities of the products formed. Chapter 2 studies the effect of the amount of reagent present in the system, Chapter 3 focuses on the geometry of molecules, while Chapter 4 deals with energy relations—most commonly elucidated by noting the effect of temperature. The next chapter focuses on a single structural feature, the carbon-carbon double bond, looking at the variety of reactions by which that double bond can be formed, or utilized for further transformations. The final chapter looks at a set of related structural features or functional groups and the mechanisms of the reactions by which one group can be converted to another.

From the beginning of the book, a variety of mechanisms of current interest in organic chemistry and biochemistry is studied. Emphasis is placed on those mechanisms that demonstrate most clearly the factors involved in even the most complex biological processes. Other books in the Chemistry–Biology Interface Series will discuss in detail catalysis—including enzyme-catalyzed reactions; macromolecules—including protein synthesis; interaction of radiation with matter—including photosynthesis; and chemical evolution—including the formation in prehistory of the molecules later incorporated in organisms. The present work attempts to lay the groundwork for the mechanistic aspects of all these fields, but leaves to the other books in the series the detailed discussion of those biochemical systems that are of central concern to molecular biologists.

Often books are written with too great an emphasis on logical arrangement, beginning with very simple examples, while the really interesting ones—if the reader ever reaches them—begin to appear in the last few chapters. This book attempts to approach the subject the other way around. We will begin with interesting examples even if they are difficult, and, for those whose interest is aroused, the explanations will appear in due course.

My thanks are due to the Danforth Foundation, whose award of an E. Harris Harbison Fellowship made possible the writing of the manuscript; to D. J. Millen of University College, London, and R. I. Reed of the University of Glasgow, for furnishing me unpublished photographs and data; to Lucille Rice at Earlham College, and Kate Korfer in Washington, D.C., for the preparation of the manuscript. The manuscript was written while my leg was in a cast—the after-effects of an automobile accident.

Otto Theodor Benfey

Contents

Introduction to Organic Reaction Mechanisms

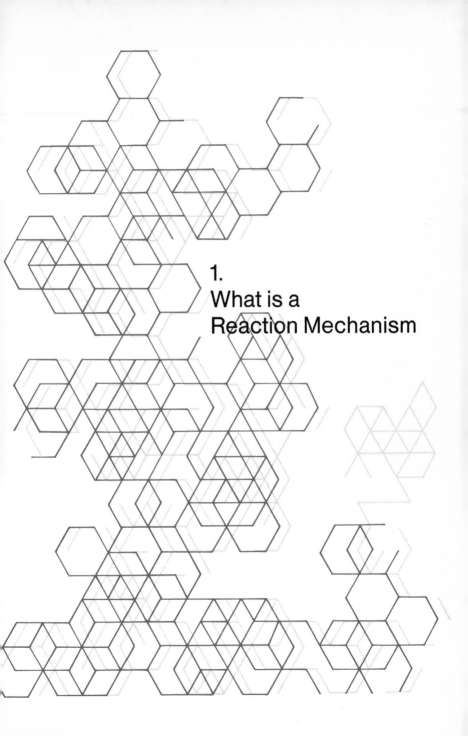

1.
What is a
Reaction Mechanism

Organic chemistry, for at least a hundred years, has been taken to mean the chemistry of carbon compounds. But what is *chemistry*? Changes in location, in space, and in time are only physical changes. Chemistry has to do with changes in "substance"—"real" changes that begin with one substance and end with another. Because of these transformations, it appears as if there is something magical about chemical phenomena. The oxygen we breathe reacts explosively with flammable hydrogen gas, and on the sides of the explosion vessel the only products found are a few drops of water. Strong, metallic iron in moist air slowly decomposes to powdery rust. Green, poisonous chlorine and shiny, metallic sodium together form white, crystalline cubes of table salt. A brown cow eats green grass and produces white milk and yellow butter. We eat animal protein and our body takes the protein apart and puts it together in a new arrangement, changing it into human protein which is useful to our growth and well-being.

Realizing the variety and complexity of changes such as these, it was hard for scientists to begin the study of chemistry, let alone know how to handle chemical phenomena quantitatively. Clearly some chemicals reacted with each other vigorously, others only slowly, still others not at all. No wonder chemistry took much longer to mature, to become a modern science, than physics.

In order to describe observed chemical reactions, analogies were used by early students of the subject, especially the familiar analogies dealing with love and hate, and with selective (or elective) affinities. Since it was found that sodium reacts violently with water, iron very slowly, and gold not at all when equal quantities of reagents were used in the comparisons, a reactivity series was set up, the most reactive metal at the top, the least at the bottom. Other metals were placed in this series and a first semiquantitative statement about metals, a "rank-order," became available in the eighteenth century.

1-1 BETWEEN START AND FINISH: WHAT HAPPENS ON THE WAY? [3,8][1]

Since the actual processes of change, the mechanisms of reactions, turned out to be extraordinarily difficult to study, early chemists contented themselves with the much simpler task of discovering what things change, leaving the nature of the changes to a later time. They discovered what substances reacted under what conditions, and they isolated one or more of the products. Beginnings and ends became known—what lay in between was as mysterious as ever. Certain patterns, however, slowly became apparent. A competent organic chemist could look at the formulas of two compounds and predict with some hope of success whether the two would react, how violently they would react, and what the product was likely to be. Organic synthesis—the production in the laboratory of a carbon compound with a given formula—was even in 1940 still considered by many as more an art than a science. By some it still is today.

1-2   THE NITRATION OF BENZENE [7]

In the 1940s, because nitration was of some interest in the production of conventional explosives such as TNT (trinitrotoluene), several groups of chemists in London and the United States successfully solved the reaction mechanism, the detailed pathway followed by the reactants, for the nitration of benzene.

We will present that mechanism here; then go into the meaning of the names, words, and symbols; and finally look into the experimental data on which the conclusions were based.

The Mechanism of the Nitration of Benzene

$$HNO_3 \; + \; H_2SO_4 \; \rightleftharpoons H_2NO_3^{\oplus} + HSO_4^{\ominus} \qquad \text{(step 1)}$$
Nitric acid   Sulfuric acid

$$H_2NO_3^{\oplus} \rightleftharpoons H_2O + NO_2^{\oplus} \qquad \text{(step 2)}$$

[1] Bracketed numbers following headings refer to suggested readings at ends of chapters.

$$H_2O + H_2SO_4 \rightleftharpoons H_3O^{\oplus} + HSO_4^{\ominus} \qquad \text{(step 3)}$$

$$NO_2^{\oplus} + C_6H_6 \rightleftharpoons C_6H_6NO_2^{\oplus} \qquad \text{(step 4)}$$
Benzene

$$C_6H_6NO_2^{\oplus} + HSO_4^{\ominus} \rightleftharpoons C_6H_5NO_2 + H_2SO_4 \qquad \text{(step 5)}$$
(or other proton acceptor B)   Nitrobenzene (or HB$^{\oplus}$)

This is a very complex set of equations and is not presented here to discourage the reader. How much of the mechanism is already comprehensible? This will depend on the reader's prior exposure to chemistry. Some fundamental terms and concepts will be presented in the following sections.

1-3 FORMULAS AND FORMAL CHARGES [1]

H_2SO_4 Sulfuric acid
HNO_3 Nitric acid
H_2O Water
$HSO_4^{\ominus}$ Bisulfate ion
$H_3O^{\oplus}$ Hydrogen ion or oxonium ion or hydronium ion or hydrated proton

$H_3O^{\oplus}$ is a proton attached to a water molecule:

$$H:\overset{\cdot\cdot}{\underset{H}{O}}: + H^{\oplus} \longrightarrow H:\overset{\oplus}{\underset{H}{\overset{\cdot\cdot}{O}}}:H$$

or

$$H-\overset{}{\underset{H}{O}}| + H^{\oplus} \longrightarrow H-\overset{\oplus}{\underset{H}{O}}-H$$

Note that in

$$H-\overset{-}{\underset{H}{O}}|$$

a line connecting two atoms is a shared electron pair, that is, a covalent bond; a line alongside an atomic symbol represents an unshared electron pair in the outer shell of the atom.

Note also that in these formulas the atomic symbols represent neither atoms nor nuclei but "kernels," that is, the nucleus plus all shells except for the outermost one. Thus if we write for the nitrogen atom $\cdot \ddot{N} \cdot$ or $\cdot \overline{N} \cdot$, the symbol N represents the atom stripped of its five outer or "valence" electrons. The N in $\cdot \overline{N} \cdot$ is a neutral atom less five electrons, or $N^{5\oplus}$. It is also the nitrogen nucleus of charge +7 together with the two electrons of the first, the K, the helium shell.

Ammonia is NH_3 and can be thought of as a combination of a nitrogen atom and three hydrogen atoms. It may be written

$$H-\overline{N}-H$$
$$|$$
$$H$$

The symbol N is still the nitrogen kernel of charge +5. Why, then, do we assume that the nitrogen and hydrogen atoms are all neutral in ammonia? As a first approximation we assume that all shared electron pairs are shared equally by the two atoms involved, that is, each atom can count as its own a half of the electron pair, or a charge of -1. We also assume that unshared electron pairs belong only to the atom that carries them. Looking now at the ammonia molecule

$$H-\overline{N}-N$$
$$|$$
$$H$$

the nitrogen symbol N has a kernel of charge +5. In its vicinity is one unshared electron pair (-2) belonging only to nitrogen, and three shared pairs each contributing a charge of -1 to the nitrogen. Now $+5 - 2 - 1 - 1 - 1 = 0$; thus the electrical environment of the nitrogen atom is neutral. The hydrogen symbol H represents a proton (hydrogen nucleus), since its electron shell is involved in bonding. There are no inner shells. A proton is a hydrogen atom lacking an electron; thus it carries a charge of $+1$. Its environment is one shared electron pair supplying the proton with a charge of -1. The net charge in the proton's environment is, therefore, zero. Charges computed in this manner are called "formal" charges since they are based on certain assumptions about the sharing of electrons.

1-4 STEP 3 OF THE NITRATION MECHANISM: WHAT MAKES A CHEMICAL AN ACID? [6a,14]

An acid, according to the Brønsted-Lowry definition, is a proton donor. The substance which accepts the proton is a base. When a substance acts as an acid in water, it donates a proton to the water as in step (3)

$$H_2SO_4 + H_2O \rightleftharpoons H_3O^{\oplus} + HSO_4^{\ominus} \qquad \text{(step 3)}$$

The fact that sulfuric acid in most aqueous solutions is completely ionized, at least to the $HSO_4^{\ominus}$ stage (it could go further:

$$HSO_4^{\ominus} + H_2O \rightleftharpoons H_3O^{\oplus} + SO_4^{2\ominus}),$$

implies that H_2SO_4 is a considerably stronger acid than water.

Why should H_2SO_4 be a stronger acid than water? In both substances the protons are attached to oxygen

$$\begin{array}{cc} & O \\ H\ O & H\ O\ S\ O \\ H & O \\ & H \end{array}$$

If we accept for the moment as dogma that 4 electron pairs around all kernels other than hydrogen endow those kernels with particular stability, we have 8 electrons to distribute in the case of water (6 from oxygen and 1 each from the 2 hydrogens) and 32 electrons in the case of the sulfuric acid molecule (6 from sulfur, 4×6 from 4 oxygen atoms, 2 from the hydrogens). Eight electrons in water must be distributed as follows

$$H\!:\!\ddot{\underset{\cdot\cdot}{O}}\!: \qquad \text{or} \qquad H\!-\!\overset{\cdot\cdot}{\underset{|}{\bar{O}}}\,| \\ \ddot{H} H$$

because only in this way are H's bonded to O, and four pairs surround the oxygen. Hydrogen attains a stable configuration with two electrons around it, in its *K* shell. Considering now the distribution of electrons in sulfuric acid, if each oxygen and sulfur atom had its own 8 electrons around it and each hydrogen 2, we would need 44 electrons. But only

32 are available. Thus 12 electrons must belong jointly to 2 bonding atoms. This gives us

The remaining electrons must belong to single atoms; they must be unshared electron pairs located so as to complete sets of four pairs per sulfur and oxygen atom.

We now compute formal charges. We can proceed as before, determining kernel charges and counting unshared electrons and half of all shared electrons; however, the following is a shortcut. The sulfur atom is a neutral, isolated atom when it has six electrons in its outer shell. In

the sulfur has only four shared electron pair bonds and no unshared electron pairs. Each of the four bonding pairs contributes a charge of -1 to the sulfur. Thus instead of a charge of -6 in the outer shell, the sulfur atom in our formula of sulfuric acid only carries a charge of -4 due to valence shell electrons. There is a deficiency of two electrons compared with the neutral state. The formal charge of sulfur is, therefore, $+2$.

If we look at the protonated oxygen atoms, they too are neutral when they can count six electrons as their own. In our formula each has four unshared electrons, supplying a charge of -4, and two shared electron pairs, each supplying a charge of -1. The net charge contributed by valence electrons shared and unshared is, therefore,

−6, the same as in the neutral atom. Each of the formal charges on the protonated oxygens is, therefore, zero.

Problem 1-1

What is the formal charge on each *un*protonated oxygen?

Answer. Again each oxygen needs a charge of −6 contributed by the valence electrons in its vicinity to achieve neutrality. In our formula for sulfuric acid, these oxygens each have six unshared electrons supplying a charge of −6, and one bonding pair supplying a further charge of −1. The total charge contributed is, therefore, −7 when only −6 is needed for neutrality. The formal charge on each of these oxygens is therefore −1.

Our formula for H_2SO_4 thus becomes

The H's are neutral as they are in the water molecule, and for the same reasons.

Perhaps we can now see why H_2SO_4 might lose protons more easily than H_2O. In both cases protons are attached to oxygen. In water the oxygen is attached to a second hydrogen, in H_2SO_4 to a doubly positive sulfur. A positive atom attracts electrons

$$S^{2\oplus} \xleftarrow{} \overset{\delta\oplus}{O} \xleftarrow{} \overset{\delta\delta\oplus}{H}$$

thus pulling them away from oxygen. (The Greek letter δ is used to designate "a fraction of." Thus δ⊕ is a partial positive charge and δδ⊕ is a smaller fraction, i.e., a fraction of a fraction.) The oxygen becomes partially electron deficient, hence slightly positive. The oxygen, in turn, attracts the electrons bonding it to hydrogen, making the hydrogen slightly positive and partially releasing it from its electrons. Proton release should, therefore, be easier than in the case of water.

We should mention here that an alternative formula for sulfuric acid may be written that recognizes the ability of third row elements to expand their valence shell capacity for electrons beyond eight. Thus sulfur can form more than four covalent bonds with oxygens

$$
\begin{array}{ccc}
& \overset{\displaystyle |\overset{\displaystyle O}{|}|}{\underset{\displaystyle |\underset{\displaystyle |}{O}{-}H}{\text{H}{-}\bar{O}{-}\overset{\oplus}{S}{-}\bar{O}|^{\ominus}}}
& \qquad
& \overset{\displaystyle |\overset{\displaystyle O}{|}|}{\underset{\displaystyle |\underset{\displaystyle |}{O}{-}{-}H}{\text{H}{-}\bar{O}{-}S{=}\bar{O}}}
\end{array}
$$

The bonding in sulfuric acid is probably partway between the singly and doubly bound forms.

1-5   STEP 1: THE PROTONATION OF NITRIC ACID [6a,14]

We can now look at step (1) of the nitration mechanism:

$$HNO_3 + H_2SO_4 \rightleftharpoons H_2NO_3{}^{\oplus} + HSO_4{}^{\ominus} \qquad \text{(step 1)}$$

Two substances conventionally spoken of as acids, because both are proton donors in water, undergo a proton transfer. The H_2SO_4 here acts as the acid, the nitric acid, HNO_3, as a base. We will write H_2SO_4 again as

Problem 1-2

Work out the formula of HNO_3 according to the principles we have discussed, given that O's are attached to N, and H to O.

Answer.   **HNO_3**. The total number of valence electrons is 24 (1 H, 5 N, 3×6 O). If each N and O had its own 8 electrons and the H 2, we would need 34 electrons. Thus the deficiency, $34 - 24 = 10$ electrons, must be involved in bonding. To bond all bonded atoms singly gives us

$$H{-}O{-}N\diagup{\diagdown}{\stackrel{O}{O}}$$

leaving two more electrons to be assigned to a bond. Two possibilities arise

$$H{-}O{=}N\diagup{\diagdown}{\stackrel{O}{O}} \quad \text{or} \quad H{-}O{-}N{\diagup\!\!\!\diagdown}{\stackrel{O}{O}}$$

If we distribute the other electrons as unshared pairs we obtain

$$H{-}\bar{\overset{\oplus}{O}}{-}\overset{\oplus}{N}{\diagdown}{\diagup}\,{\overset{\ominus}{\bar{\underset{\ominus}{\bar{O}}}}}\, \quad \text{or} \quad H{-}\bar{O}{-}\overset{\oplus}{N}{\diagup\!\!\!\diagdown}{\overset{\bar{O}}{\underset{\ominus}{O}}}$$

$$\text{I} \qquad\qquad\qquad \text{II}$$

Of the above formulas, II is much more plausible for the following reasons. Firstly, there are fewer charges. The creation—meaning separation—of $\oplus$ and $\ominus$ charges always requires energy. Secondly, formula I has two $\oplus$ charges on adjacent atoms which involves considerable repulsion and is avoided in formula II.

The acid-base reaction then becomes

$$H{-}\bar{O}{-}\overset{\overset{\overset{\ominus}{\bar{O}}}{|}}{\underset{\underset{O{-}H}{|}}{S}}{}^{2\oplus}{-}\bar{O}^{\ominus} \; + \; H{-}\bar{O}{-}\overset{\oplus}{N}{\diagup\!\!\!\diagdown}{\overset{\bar{O}}{\underset{\ominus}{O}}} \; \longrightarrow \; H_2NO_3{}^{\oplus} \; + \; {}^{\ominus}\bar{O}{-}\overset{\overset{\overset{\ominus}{\bar{O}}}{|}}{\underset{\underset{O{-}H}{|}}{S}}{}^{2\oplus}{-}\bar{O}^{\ominus}$$

We must ask where the extra proton is located in $H_2NO_3{}^{\oplus}$. It can link to any unshared electron pair, all of which are on oxygen atoms. Possibilities are

$$H{-}\overset{\oplus}{O}{-}\overset{\oplus}{N}{\diagup\!\!\!\diagdown}{\overset{\bar{O}}{\underset{\ominus}{\bar{O}}}}\,\underset{H}{|} \quad \text{and} \quad H{-}\bar{O}{-}\overset{\oplus}{N}{\diagup\!\!\!\diagdown}{\overset{\bar{O}}{O{-}H}}$$

$$\text{III} \qquad\qquad\qquad \text{IV}$$

Of these the second is far more plausible, but we know that protons on oxygen are extremely mobile so that there is probably a rapid equilibrium established between them, with the preponderance of the protonated nitric acid being in form **IV**.

Why then is H_2SO_4 a stronger acid than HNO_3 so that the former supplies the proton to the latter? We could account for it by formal charge again, the +2 on S being a stronger electron attractor than the +1 on N. In general it is found that in the series

$$
\begin{array}{cccc}
\text{O—H} & \text{O—H} & \text{O} & \text{O} \\
| & | & | & | \\
\text{H—O—Si—O—H} & \text{H—O—P—O} & \text{H—O—S—O} & \text{H—O—Cl—O} \\
| & | & | & | \\
\text{O—H} & \text{O—H} & \text{O—H} & \text{O}
\end{array}
$$

the acid strength strongly increases as we go to perchloric acid, $HClO_4$, on the right. The Cl in $HClO_4$ carries a formal charge of +3, S +2, P +1, Si 0. We can think of this series from left to right as one where we progressively pull protons off oxygen atoms (using hypothetical "nuclear forceps," as someone recently put it) and fuse them into the central nucleus, thus increasing its atomic number by one. Nitric acid admittedly does not exist as H_3NO_4 but only in the dehydrated form HNO_3. The formal charge on N, however, remains +1, as is that of P in H_3PO_4, so that the formal charge argument may well be sufficient to account for the difference in acid strength.

The proposed mechanism, therefore, claims that when benzene is placed in a mixture of concentrated nitric and sulfuric acids, the benzene does not react with either acid. Instead, a proton transfer from sulfuric to nitric acid occurs in the mixture of acids.

1-6 STEP 2: FORMATION OF THE NITRONIUM ION— GEOMETRY AND RAMAN SPECTRUM [2,4,6*b*,7,9,13]

It is now proposed that the protonated nitric acid breaks down as shown in step (2)

$$H_2NO_3^{\oplus} \rightarrow H_2O + NO_2^{\oplus} \qquad \text{(step 2)}$$

forming an ion, $NO_2^{\oplus}$, called the nitronium ion.

If we look at the two forms of $H_2NO_3^\oplus$ again (formulas III and IV) we recognize that the ion III can split into these two fragments and we can see why the split might occur. The repulsion between two neighboring positive charges may lead to the breakup of the ion if the two fragments have reasonable stability.

The electrons in the bond that breaks stay with the oxygen forming a molecule of water. [This, in the presence of strong acids, is protonated to $H_3O^\oplus$; see step (3).] Some rearrangement of electrons is likely to occur on the $NO_2^\oplus$ side to re-form the sets of four electron pairs around each atom. The nitrogen loses an electron pair to the oxygen of the incipient water molecule and must gain one to regain stability. The negatively charged oxygen can share one of its unshared pairs

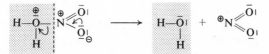

permitting the nitrogen to continue to have four electron pairs around it. Let us examine this $NO_2^\oplus$ ion in more detail.

$$\overset{\oplus}{N}\!\!\diagup^{\bar{\underset{}{O}}\text{I}}_{\underset{}{O}\text{I}} \quad \text{or} \quad \bar{\underset{}{O}}\!=\!\overset{\oplus}{N}\!=\!\bar{\underset{}{O}} \quad \text{or} \quad \overset{\oplus}{N}\!=\!\bar{\underset{}{O}}$$

We might first ask what it reminds us of. The central nitrogen nucleus contains seven protons and some neutrons. The number of electrons in the ion is one less than the number of protons in the nucleus—hence the ionic charge of +1. Suppose, in our imagination, we again use our "nuclear forceps" and pull a proton out of the nitrogen nucleus. We will be left with a carbon nucleus and one less nuclear charge.

$$\bar{\underset{}{O}}\!=\!\overset{\oplus}{N}\!=\!\bar{\underset{}{O}} \xrightarrow{\text{nuclear forceps}} \bar{\underset{}{O}}\!=\!C\!=\!\bar{\underset{}{O}} + \text{proton}$$

Thus $NO_2^\oplus$ should have some of the properties of carbon dioxide, such as the geometry of the electron arrangement around the atomic kernels. An added proton in the central nucleus should not affect the electronic distribution. What, then, is the most compact packing of four electron pairs around a nucleus, remembering that the pairs are negatively charged and want to stay as far apart from each other as possible? Two distributions suggest themselves—one in two dimensions, the other in three.

In two dimensions the maximum angle between four pairs equidistant from a central point would be 90°. The four electron pairs would be situated

at the corners of a square. But there should be more space available if the four pairs can spread out in all three dimensions of space.

If we think of each electron pair as requiring an approximately spherical region, we can build a model in which attraction to the nucleus is represented by stretched rubber bands and the electrons by Styrofoam spheres, as in Fig. 1-1. A three-dimensional, tetrahedral arrangement of the electron pairs allows the electrons to be closer to the nucleus while the angle between the electrons is extended to the tetrahedral angle of $109\frac{1}{2}°$ instead of the planar 90°.

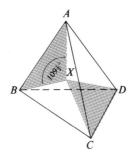

(a)

(b)

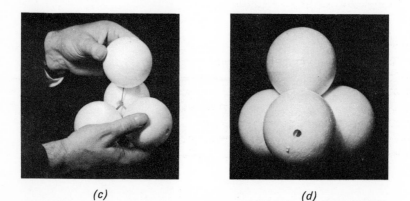
(c)   *(d)*

Fig. 1-1. A tetrahedral arrangement allows spheres to pack more closely than a square arrangement. [Reproduced with permission from L. C. King, Chemistry, 37:12 (Feb. 1964).]

One of the interesting properties of a tetrahedron is that the plane AXB is at right angles to the plane CXD. This can be seen most easily by inscribing a tetrahedron $ABCD$ in a cube, when lines AB and CD are opposite diagonals at right angles to each other.

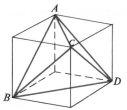

If we look at the molecule O=C=O and the ion O=$\overset{\oplus}{N}$=O from this geometrical point of view, we will have to arrange a tetrahedron of electron pairs around each atom. The double bonds, then, represent a shared edge of two tetrahedrons.

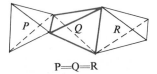

P=Q=R

Using tetrahedrons or spheres to construct our model, the geometry of CO_2 and $NO_2^{\oplus}$ turns out to be linear. Both are highly symmetrical entities which have an interesting property. During their "breathing vibration," that is, a vibration in which the dimensions of the structure increase and decrease without changing the structure's shape, there is no change in dipole moment. For a neutral molecule the dipole moment is something like a magnetic moment; it measures the extent of the polarity of the molecule. For a structure

$$\overset{+z}{\bullet}\underset{d}{\rule{3cm}{0.4pt}}\overset{-z}{\bullet}$$

the dipole moment equals charge multiplied by the distance between the centers of charge, $DM = z \times d$. For a polar molecule such as $\overset{\delta\oplus}{H}$—$\overset{\delta\ominus}{Cl}$, the breathing vibration stretches the molecule, and increases the dipole moment. The frequencies of molecular vibrations can usually be observed in the infrared spectrum or the Raman spectrum. In the latter a beam of single-wavelength radiation is directed onto the material under study and some of the transmitted radiation has a frequency higher or lower than that of the incident beam by an amount equal to one of the frequencies of vibration of the material. One difference between Raman and infrared spectra is that highly symmetrical vibrations, such as the breathing vibrations of CO_2 or $NO_2^\oplus$, do not appear on the infrared spectrum but do appear on the Raman spectrum. Carbon dioxide, if linear, has a zero dipole moment throughout its breathing vibration. The centers of positive and negative charge are coincident at the center of the molecule throughout.

$$O=C=O \qquad\qquad O=C=O \qquad\qquad O=C=O$$

If carbon dioxide were bent (as sulfur dioxide, $^\ominus\!|\underline{O}|\ \overset{\oplus}{\underset{\diagup\ \diagdown}{S}}\ |\underline{O}|$, is) its breathing vibration would change its dipole moment (magnitude and direction are indicated by a crossed arrow).

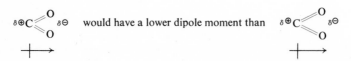

The lack of a frequency in the infrared and its presence in the Raman spectrum is, therefore, a very sensitive indication of the presence of a highly symmetrical entity. Such a frequency is found at 1400 cm^{-1} (1400 waves per centimeter) when the Raman spectrum of mixtures of nitric and sulfuric acids is observed. It also appears, but with much weaker intensity, in Raman spectra of pure nitric acid, suggesting the reaction sequence

$$HNO_3 + HNO_3 \rightarrow H_2NO_3^\oplus + NO_3^\ominus$$

$$H_2NO_3^\oplus \rightarrow H_2O + NO_2^\oplus$$

The line appears more intense when N_2O_5 is dissolved in nitric acid, implying the ionization of N_2O_5 (see Fig. 1-2)

$$N_2O_5 \rightarrow NO_2^\oplus + NO_3^\ominus$$

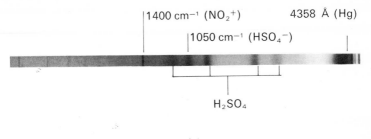

(a)

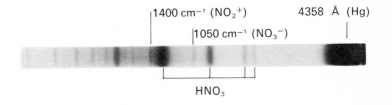

(b)

Fig. 1-2. Raman spectra (a) of mixture of nitric and sulfuric acids, (b) of N_2O_5 in anhydrous nitric acid, showing the 1400 cm^{-1} line due to $NO_2^{\oplus}$, the 1050 cm^{-1} line [due to $HSO_4^{\ominus}$ in (a) and $NO_3^{\ominus}$ in (b)] and the mercury (Hg) line used as incident radiation. (Courtesy D. J. Millen, University College, London.)

A second frequency at 1050 cm^{-1} also appears, which is assigned to $NO_3^{\ominus}$. (Unfortunately it is also the frequency of $HSO_4^{\ominus}$.) The 1050 cm^{-1} line is present in the pure HNO_3 and the HNO_3–H_2SO_4 spectra, but is absent when HNO_3 is dissolved in $HClO_4$. Instead the frequency of $ClO_4^{\ominus}$ (as in $NaClO_4$) appears together with the 1400 cm^{-1} $NO_2^{\ominus}$ frequency.

$$HNO_3 + 2\,HClO_4 \rightarrow NO_2^{\oplus} + H_3O^{\oplus} + 2\,ClO_4^{\ominus}$$

Later on we will give further evidence for the $NO_2^{\oplus}$ ion, including the discovery that $NO_2^{\oplus}$ can be the cation in stable crystalline salts such as nitronium perchlorate, $NO_2^{\oplus}ClO_4^{\ominus}$. For the moment we will assume its presence in the nitrating mixture and will examine the steps by which the $NO_2^{\oplus}$ ion is believed to become attached to carbon in nitrobenzene.

1-7 STEPS 4 AND 5: THE ATTACK ON BENZENE [6*b*,7,10,11]

The equations we wrote were

$$C_6H_6 + NO_2^{\oplus} \rightleftharpoons C_6H_6NO_2^{\oplus} \qquad \text{(step 4)}$$
Benzene

$$C_6H_6NO_2^{\oplus} + HSO_4^{\ominus} \rightarrow C_6H_5NO_2 + H_2SO_4 \qquad \text{(step 5)}$$
Nitrobenzene

It might be asked (and was asked) why two steps are needed. Could not the entering $NO_2^{\oplus}$ push out the extra proton with or without a base, B, as shown below?

$$NO_2^{\oplus} + C_6H_6 + B \longrightarrow \underset{\substack{\text{Halfway stage} \\ \text{of single process}}}{\overset{NO_2^{\oplus}}{\underset{B\text{---}H}{\diagdown}} C_6H_5} \longrightarrow C_6H_5NO_2 + BH^{\oplus}$$

The answer was supplied by L. Melander in 1949. It had been known for some time that if isotopes of hydrogen were used in reactions involving the breaking of C—H bonds, the reactions would be slowed down. The use of deuterium (D or ^{2}H) would slow down the reaction by factors from 3 to 12, the use of tritium (T or ^{3}H) by factors from 5 to 30. Thus if we nitrated benzene containing one or two tritium atoms and the breaking of C—H or C—T bonds was part of the nitration step, then the $NO_2^{\oplus}$ should preferentially attack carbon atoms attached to H rather than to T because C—H bonds would be broken more easily. Within the limits of experimental error in Melander's studies, however, the $NO_2^{\oplus}$ attacked the carbons of C—T bonds as rapidly as those of C—H bonds, suggesting that the C—T and C—H bonds were not broken in the nitrating step. Presumably these bonds were broken in a fast follow-up step while the attack of $NO_2^{\oplus}$ on benzene was slow and determined the rate of the overall reaction. The accepted reaction sequence then is, as was stated earlier

$$C_6H_6 + NO_2^{\oplus} \rightleftharpoons C_6H_6NO_2^{\oplus} \qquad \text{(step 4)}$$

$$C_6H_6NO_2^{\oplus} + HSO_4^{\ominus} \rightarrow C_6H_5NO_2 + H_2SO_4 \qquad \text{(step 5)}$$

1-8 THE PECULIAR CHARACTER OF BENZENE [12,15]

It is time that we looked in detail at the organic portion of this reaction, the C_6H_6, since our major concern in this book is with organic reaction mechanisms. There are more than a million carbon compounds known, and a little over a hundred years ago, in 1858, the German chemist August Kekulé and the Scotsman Archibald Couper discovered the secret of carbon's prodigality. They agreed that carbon had a valence of four and then proposed that carbon atoms had an unusual capacity to link with each other. These two principles alone account for the formulas of numerous known compounds, such as the series of similar hydrocarbons CH_4, C_2H_6, C_3H_8

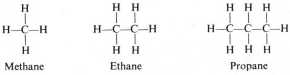

Methane   Ethane   Propane

or the series of the alcohols CH_3OH, C_2H_5OH, and the two of formula C_3H_7OH

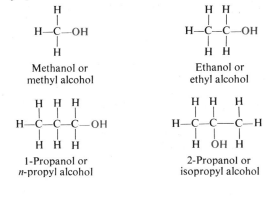

Methanol or
methyl alcohol

Ethanol or
ethyl alcohol

1-Propanol or
n-propyl alcohol

2-Propanol or
isopropyl alcohol

The last two are known as isomers—they have the same molecular formula but different structural formulas which correspond to two different compounds of boiling points 97.2°C and 82.3°C, respectively.

One of the hopes implicit in the structural theory enunciated by Kekulé and Couper was that for every separate formula that could be drawn there would be a distinct, pure chemical found one day in nature or synthesized in the laboratory. Benzene presented a problem. It was known to contain an equal number of carbon and hydrogen atoms, and this number was accepted as six by those who were convinced that Avogadro's law, which stated that equal volumes of gases at the same temperature and pressure contained equal numbers of molecules, was valid. For example, 32 g of oxygen at 0°C and one atm pressure occupy 22.4 liters, and if we join chemists in arbitrarily taking 16 as the atomic weight of oxygen, then 32 is the molecular weight of the oxygen molecule, O_2. Since an oxygen molecule is an extremely small entity, 32 g of oxygen must contain a very large number of O_2 molecules, say N. An equal volume of another gas, such as methane, should contain the same number N molecules of methane. The relative weight of N molecules of methane to N molecules oxygen should give the relative weight of 1 molecule of methane to 1 molecule of oxygen. Now 22.4 liters of methane at 0°C and 1 atm weigh 16 g, just half the weight of an equal volume of oxygen. Therefore, 1 molecule of methane must weigh one-half the weight of 1 molecule of oxygen, or $\frac{1}{2}(32) = 16$. With $C = 12$ and $H = 1$ this makes methane's formula CH_4.

Benzene is a solid at 0°C and a liquid at room temperature, but its vapor can be weighed above its boiling point (80°C) and compared with the weight of an equal volume of oxygen at the same temperature. The molecular weight is found to be 78, more than twice the molecular weight of oxygen. Since benzene has equal numbers of carbon and hydrogen atoms, $(CH)_n$, $n = 6$ since $6 \times (12 + 1) = 78$. Benzene's formula is, therefore, C_6H_6 and we return to the question of its structural formula. Numerous ones can be written in which each carbon has a valence of four such as:

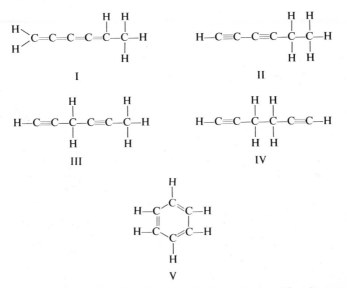

I II III IV V

One of the peculiarities of benzene is that only one chlorobenzene, C_6H_5Cl, one bromobenzene, C_6H_5Br, and one nitrobenzene, $C_6H_5NO_2$, have ever been prepared. Formulas I, II, III, and IV should all give at least two different compounds C_6H_5X. Admittedly one can devise an open-chain molecule with all H atoms alike such as

$$\text{H}-\overset{\displaystyle\text{H}}{\underset{\displaystyle\text{H}}{\text{C}}}-\text{C}\equiv\text{C}-\text{C}\equiv\text{C}-\overset{\displaystyle\text{H}}{\underset{\displaystyle\text{H}}{\text{C}}}-\text{H}$$

but another peculiarity also needs to be accounted for. The open-chain molecules should all take on four H_2 molecules to react at its double or triple bonds

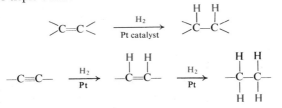

Benzene, however, only takes on three H_2 molecules

$$C_6H_6 \quad \xrightarrow[\text{Pt}]{3\,H_2} \quad C_6H_{12}$$

An answer came to Kekulé in 1865 while he was staring into the fire of his fireplace. In 1858 he had envisioned the atoms whirling around before him, when suddenly they seemed to link up, giving him the idea of the chain formation of carbon atoms. This time he was attempting to make sense of the ever-growing body of benzene derivatives and their peculiar properties:

"I was sitting writing at my textbook but the work did not progress; my thoughts were elsewhere. I turned my chair to the fire and dozed. Again the atoms were gamboling before my eyes. This time the smaller groups kept modestly in the background. My mental eye, rendered more acute by repeated visions of the kind, could now distinguish larger structures of manifold conformation; long rows, sometimes more closely fitted together, all twining and twisting in snake-like motion. But look! What was that? One of the snakes had seized hold of its own tail, and the form whirled mockingly before my eyes. As if by a flash of lightning I awoke; and this time also I spent the rest of the night in working out the consequences of the hypothesis."

So future chemists do not think that all that is needed for scientific fame is visions in front of the fireplace, Kekulé added:

"Let us learn to dream, gentlemen, then perhaps we shall find the truth. But let us beware of publishing our dreams till they have been tested by the waking understanding."[1]

The formula of benzene proposed by Kekulé was formula V:

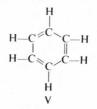

V

---

[1] F. A. Kekulé, *Ber.*, **23**:1302 (1890); F. R. Japp (trans.) in O. T. Benfey, *J. Chem. Educ.*, **35**:21 (1958).

It explained why a molecule of benzene took on only three molecules of hydrogen

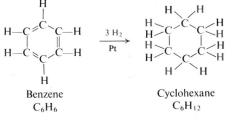

Benzene
C_6H_6

Cyclohexane
C_6H_{12}

and, since all the hydrogens are equivalent, why only one derivative C_6H_5X could be made.

The disubstituted benzenes provided some difficulty because only three compounds $C_6H_4X_2$ were found. These could, after a few years, be assigned to the 1,2-, 1,3-, and 1,4-derivatives

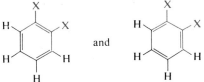

1,2-   1,3-   1,4-

If, however, we look at the 1,2- formula in detail, we discover that, by the structural theory, two substances are expected corresponding to

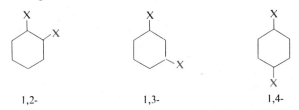

and

the first having a double bond between the substituted carbons, the second a single bond. Such a pair of isomers has never been isolated and it represents a serious failure of the structural theory. Whenever two formulas are written that differ only in bond or electron positions while the atoms remain interconnected according to the same pattern (i.e., no pair of atoms connected in one formula is disconnected in the other), then only a single substance is found in nature. Some other examples are

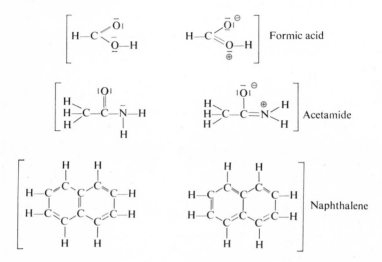

Kekulé had a simple answer to the $C_6H_4X_2$ problem. He suggested that the two forms interchange so rapidly that it was impossible to isolate either of the forms. The modern explanation, part of the *theory of resonance*, may be put in the form that electron-position isomers cannot exist; that formulas differing only in electron positions and not significantly in nuclear positions do not correspond to separate substances but are approximations of the structure of a single substance. One way of stating the theory is to say that when two or more positions are available to an electron without affecting the nuclear pattern, the electrons tend to spread out over all the permitted positions rather than choosing among them. For electrons to "spread out" we have to think of them as smeared-out charge clouds or as imaginable only over a period of time over which they have covered much territory—just as the circular appearance of a rapidly rotating propeller represents the time-averaged appearance of a propeller of very different shape. Since a propeller can be turned off we are able to discover its real shape. With electrons we are not so fortunate. Only a time average is available to us, and we will probably never know whether the "real" electron in a molecule is whizzing around or is smeared out. It makes no difference (that is, the measurable effects are the same), hence, both models are acceptable and used.

According to the theory of resonance the actual substance has its electrons spread over all permitted positions. Applied to the $C_6H_4X_2$ example we may write

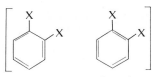 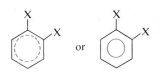

Structural theory formulas   Resonance formulations

and in the case of formic acid

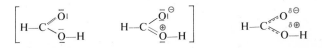

Since a molecule of benzene itself can be written in two ways, we expect a resonance formulation here also

The theory of resonance accounts for a significant property of benzene. Its classic formula depicted it as containing three double bonds. One of the most characteristic properties of carbon—carbon double bonds is that they tend to add Br_2, HNO_3, HI, and many other reagents.

$$H_2C=CH_2 \xrightarrow{Br_2} \underset{\underset{Br \quad Br}{|\quad\quad|}}{H_2C-CH_2}$$

$$H_2C{=}CH_2 \xrightarrow{HNO_3} H_2\underset{H}{\overset{}{C}}{-}\underset{ONO_2}{\overset{}{C}}H_2$$

$$H_2C{=}CH_2 \xrightarrow{HI} H_2\underset{H}{\overset{}{C}}{-}\underset{I}{\overset{}{C}}H_2$$

Benzene heated with HNO_3 does *not* add this molecule. Nor does it add bromine, unless irradiated by sunlight. These reagents act on benzene by substitution instead, leaving its double bonds (assuming it has any) intact.

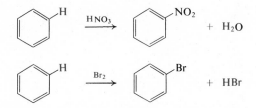

Resonance theory says that the double bonds in benzene are "delocalized" and gain a certain measure of stability by this delocalization. When the nitronium ion attacks benzene it does localize an electron pair in step (4), but the pair is delocalized again when the intermediate

$$C_6H_5{\overset{H}{\underset{NO_2}{\overset{\displaystyle\oplus}{\big<}}}}$$

loses its proton.

1-9 THE ATTACK ON BENZENE (CONTINUED) [6*b*,7]

Our detailed mechanism for steps (4) and (5) now become the following, written (*a*) classically

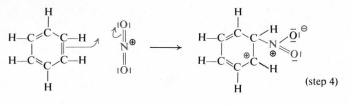

(step 4)

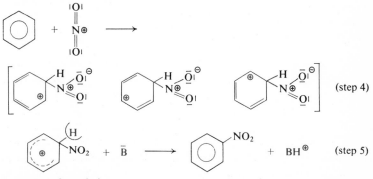

(step 5)

or (*b*) written in a more modern, abbreviated form

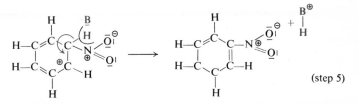

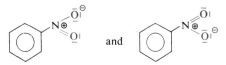

(step 4)

(step 5)

Resonance formulation
equivalent to the three
forms shown in brackets
in previous line

One footnote needs to be added. The NO_2 group attached to benzene
can also be written in two ways:

Resonance theory predicts that the actual form is a combination of
the two and, in fact, the two nitrogen—oxygen bonds are identical
in length and bond strength. Nitrobenzene is, therefore, written
more accurately as

All the steps of the nitration of benzene have now been presented in detail and we will end this chapter with some further techniques and data that have confirmed the nitration mechanism. They may also suggest approaches to the elucidation of other reactions.

1-10 FURTHER EVIDENCE FOR THE INTERMEDIATE $NO_2^{\oplus}$ ION [5,7]

A. Freezing-point Depression Studies

In dilute solutions, the freezing point of solvents is lowered by the same amount by very different substances as long as the same number of particles of solute are present. This is a general phenomenon known for many decades and is one of the "colligative properties," that is, one of those properties depending only on the *number* of particles in solution and not on their nature.

Thus when one mole of glycerol (glycerine) or ethylene glycol (antifreeze, $HOCH_2CH_2OH$) is dissolved in 1,000 g of water the freezing point of water is lowered from 0°C to about −1.8°C. We speak of this figure as the *molal freezing-point depression constant* of water and define it as the freezing point lowering of the solvent produced by one mole of solute dissolved in 1,000 g of solvent. When one mole of sodium chloride is dissolved in 1,000 g of water, the depression is not −1.8°C but almost twice as much, namely −3.4°C. This is accounted for by the assumption that each mole of NaCl produces two moles of particles—NaCl in water exists in the form of separate ions, $Na^{\oplus}$ and $Cl^{\ominus}$. When more dilute solutions of glycerol and NaCl are compared the freezing point ratio approaches 2:1 more closely.

Sulfuric acid freezes at 10.4°C and has a freezing point depression constant of 6.12°C. Substances that do not ionize or otherwise react with sulfuric acid—such as chlorosulfuric acid, $ClSO_3H$—lower the freezing point by this amount so that the observed freezing point is 4.3°C when a mole of solute is dissolved in 1,000 g of sulfuric acid. Nitric acid produces four times this depression. A simple protonation according to step (1)

$$HNO_3 + H_2SO_4 \rightarrow H_2NO_3^{\oplus} + HSO_4^{\ominus} \qquad \text{(step 1)}$$

would only produce two particles per molecule of HNO_3 and, therefore, a double depression. The further dissociation

$$H_2NO_3^{\oplus} \rightarrow H_2O + NO_2^{\oplus} \qquad \text{(step 2)}$$

followed by protonation of water

$$H_2O + H_2SO_4 \rightarrow H_3O^{\oplus} + HSO_4^{\ominus} \qquad \text{(step 3)}$$

produces a total of four particles per molecule of HNO_3

$$HNO_3 + 2\,H_2SO_4 \rightarrow NO_2^{\oplus} + H_3O^{\oplus} + 2\,HSO_4^{\ominus} \qquad (1\text{-}1)$$

The fact that the observed depression is four times the depression constant implies that, at least in dilute solution, nitric acid is completely dissociated according to Eq. (1-1). There are few other processes which give a fourfold depression and none are as plausible as the formation of the $NO_2^{\oplus}$ ion.

When nitrogen pentoxide, N_2O_5, the anhydride of nitric acid ($2\,HNO_3$ minus $H_2O = N_2O_5$), is dissolved in sulfuric acid, the depression is even higher, being 6 times the value expected for non-dissociating solutes. The depression is explained by

$$N_2O_5 + 3\,H_2SO_4 \rightarrow 2\,NO_2^{\oplus} + H_3O^{\oplus} + 3\,HSO_4^{\ominus} \qquad (1\text{-}2)$$

Problem 1-3

It has been suggested that N_2O_5 first ionizes to $NO_2^{\oplus}$ and $NO_3^{\ominus}$. Show that this is consistent with Eq. (1-2).

Answer. If

$$N_2O_5 \rightarrow NO_2^{\oplus} + NO_3^{\ominus} \qquad (1\text{-}3)$$

then in concentrated sulfuric acid, $NO_3^{\ominus}$ will be protonated first to HNO_3 and then to $H_2NO_3^{\oplus}$, which will again yield $NO_2^{\oplus}$ according to step (2)

$$NO_3^{\ominus} + 2\ H_2SO_4 \rightarrow H_2NO_3^{\oplus} + 2\ HSO_4^{\ominus} \qquad (1\text{-}4)$$

$$H_2NO_3^{\oplus} \rightarrow H_2O + NO_2^{\oplus} \qquad (1\text{-}5)$$

$$H_2O + H_2SO_4 \rightarrow H_3O^{\oplus} + HSO_4^{\ominus} \qquad (1\text{-}6)$$

Adding these four equations we obtain Eq. (1-2).

B. Synthesis of Nitronium Salts

If the $NO_2^{\oplus}$ ion is formed in large concentrations when HNO_3 is dissolved in H_2SO_4, and if $NO_2^{\oplus}$ has the compact, linear structure of the stable carbon dioxide molecule, it is at least plausible to suspect that under suitable conditions salts of the $NO_2^{\oplus}$ ion might be isolated. Hantzsch in the 1920s showed that nitric and perchloric acids react to form solid salt-like compounds which he believed to be salts of the protonated nitric acid $H_2NO_3^{\oplus}ClO_4^{\ominus}$ and even $(H_3NO_3^{2\oplus})$-$2(ClO_4^{\ominus})$. Work by Ingold and co-workers (University College, London) in the 1940s demonstrated that the products were actually mixtures of $H_3O^{\oplus}ClO_4^{\ominus}$ and $NO_2^{\oplus}ClO_4^{\ominus}$ formed by the reaction

$$HNO_3 + 2\ HClO_4 \rightarrow NO_2^{\oplus} + H_3O^{\oplus} + 2\ ClO_4^{\ominus}$$

By using nitromethane, CH_3NO_2, as a solvent, the pure nitronium salt $NO_2^{\oplus}ClO_4^{\ominus}$ could be separated and crystallized. It is a white crystalline solid which, of course, reacts with water. Its Raman spectrum is simply that of the $NO_2^{\oplus}$ ion plus that of the perchlorate ion.

Both this salt and solid N_2O_5 have been examined by x-ray crystallography and the linear form of the $NO_2^{\oplus}$ ion is confirmed in both cases. Solid N_2O_5 in fact is nitronium nitrate $NO_2^{\oplus}NO_3^{\ominus}$, so that this nitronium salt has been known for decades without our being aware of its ionic nature. The crystal structure obtained for N_2O_5 is shown in Fig. 1-3.

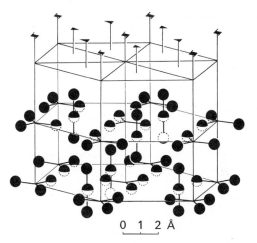

Fig. 1-3. Crystal structure of N_2O_5 *showing linear* NO_2 *and flat trigonal* NO_3 *units (the N in the center of the* NO_3 *units is not shown). [From Grison, Ericks, and de Vries, Acta Crystallogr., 3:293 (1950); reproduced with permission.]*

SUGGESTED READINGS

1. Benfey, O. T.: "The Names and Structures of Organic Compounds," chaps. 13, 14, John Wiley & Sons, Inc., New York, 1966.
2. Bent, H. A.: The Tetrahedral Atom, *Chemistry*, **39**:8 (Dec. 1966); **40**:8 (Jan. 1967).
3. Campbell, J. A.: "Why Do Chemical Reactions Occur?" Prentice-Hall, Inc., Englewood Cliffs, N.J., 1965.
4. Dyer, J. R.: "Applications of Absorption Spectroscopy of Organic Compounds," Prentice-Hall, Inc., Englewood Cliffs, N.J., 1965.
5. Gillespie, R. J.: Cryoscopy—What We Can Learn from Freezing Points, *Chemistry*, **38**:12 (Oct. 1965).
6. Hine, J.: "Physical Organic Chemistry," 2d ed., (*a*) chap. 2; (*b*) chap. 16, McGraw-Hill Book Company, New York, 1962.

7. Ingold, C. K.: "Structure and Mechanism in Organic Chemistry," chap. 6, Cornell University Press, Ithaca, N.Y., 1953.

8. King, E. L.: "How Chemical Reactions Occur," W. A. Benjamin Co., New York, 1963.

9. King, L. C.: Molecular Architecture, *Chemistry*, **37**:12 (Feb. 1964).

10. Melander, L.: "Isotope Effects on Reaction Rates," The Ronald Press Company, New York, 1960.

11. Semenov, D. A., and J. D. Roberts: Use of Isotopes in Organic Chemistry, *J. Chem. Educ.*, **33**:2 (1956).

12. van Tamelen, E.: Benzene—the Story of Its Formulas, *Chemistry*, **38**:6 (Jan. 1965).

13. Tobias, R. S.: Raman Spectroscopy in Inorganic Chemistry, Parts 1 and 2, *J. Chem. Educ.*, **44**:1, 70 (1967).

14. VanderWerf, C. A.: "Acids, Bases and the Chemistry of the Covalent Bond," Reinhold Publishing Corporation, New York, 1961.

15. Wheland, G. W.: "Resonance in Organic Chemistry," John Wiley & Sons, Inc., New York, 1955.

16. White, E. H.: "Chemical Background for the Biological Sciences," Prentice-Hall, Inc., Englewood Cliffs, N.J., 1964.

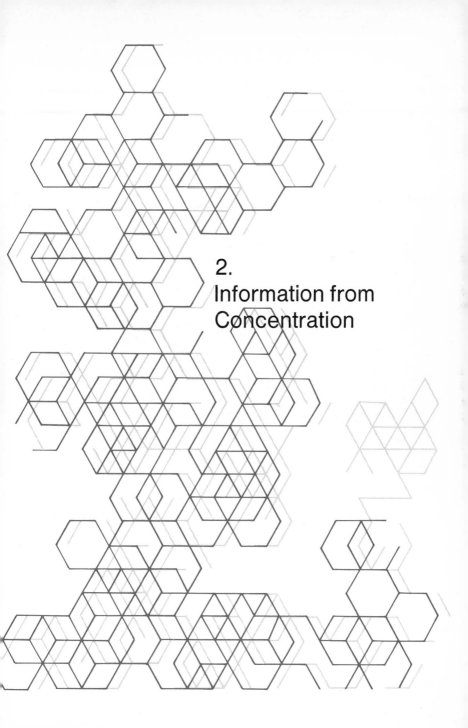

2.
Information from
Concentration

2-1 INTRODUCTION [1,2,3,4a,6a]

One of the most startling discoveries about the nitration reaction was that on reacting benzene with excess nitric acid using nitromethane as a solvent, a change in the concentration of benzene does not affect the rate—that is, the yield of nitrobenzene per unit time is independent of the amount of benzene initially present. Even more remarkable is the observation that benzene is nitrated at a constant rate from the start of the reaction when it is at its maximum concentration to the end when it is all gone (Fig. 2-1). The figure illustrates "zero-order kinetics" because the rate of reaction is constant, independent of changes in concentration of reagents.

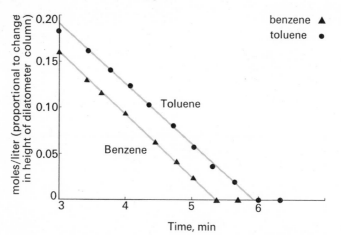

Fig. 2-1. Plot of change in concentration of reagents against time for nitration of benzene and toluene under conditions given in Table 2-1, showing zero-order kinetics. Linear and parallel slopes mean rate of change of concentration is constant (and identical for benzene and toluene) until reaction is complete, in spite of decreasing concentration of reagent. (Courtesy R. I. Reed, University of Glasgow.)

One way of following the reaction is to observe its volume. The products have a smaller volume than the reactants so that careful observation of the level of materials in a uniform tube above the reaction vessel yields us information about the reaction. At a carefully controlled, constant temperature the volume readings in Table 2-1 were recorded using the apparatus known as a dilatometer (volume-measuring device) which is depicted in Fig. 2-2. The temperature must be controlled carefully because even very slight temperature

Table 2-1   Volume Readings in the Nitration of Benzene and Toluene in Nitromethane, Showing Identical Rates within Experimental Error (see Fig. 2-1) and No Variation in Rate during the Reaction

Time t		h cm (dilatometer scale)	Time t		h cm (dilatometer scale)
min	sec		min	sec	
A *Benzene nitration.*[a] 0.35M C_6H_6, 12.4M HNO_3, 0.497M HNO_2, 10.7°C			B *Toluene nitration.* 0.33M $C_6H_5CH_3$, 12.4M HNO_3, 0.497M HNO_2, 10.7°C		
3	20	23.80	3	00	24.02
3	40	23.26	3	20	23.66
4	00	22.73	3	40	23.10
4	20	22.21	4	00	22.47
4	40	17.91	4	20	21.88
5	00	17.38	4	40	21.31
5	20	16.85	5	00	20.71
5	40	16.87	5	20	20.06
6	00	16.86	5	40	19.51
			6	00	18.92
			6	20	18.95

[a] Nitrous acid, HNO_2, is added to prevent uncontrolled side reactions.
Courtesy R. I. Reed, University of Glasgow.

changes can significantly alter the volume readings, or more generally, the rates of reactions.

It is one of the most generally held beliefs of chemists that concentration does have an influence on rates of reactions because reagents must collide to react—assuming at least two reagents are involved. Assuming that collisions are necessary for reaction, doubling

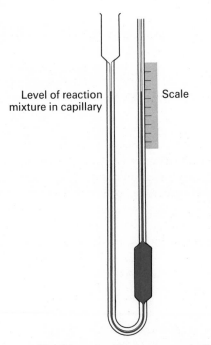

Level of reaction mixture in capillary

Scale

Fig. 2-2. A dilatometer—used for studying reactions by following volume changes. [After G. A. Benford and C. K. Ingold, J. Chem. Soc., 932 (1938).]

the concentration of a reagent A in a reaction A + B → products should double the number of collisions with B, or in general

No. of collisions of A and B ∝ [A]

Similarly if [B], the concentration of B, is varied,

No. of collisions of A and B ∝ [B]

If both are varied,

No. of collisions of A and B ∝ [A][B]

If we assume further that at a given temperature a fixed fraction of collisions has the proper orientation and the requisite minimum energy for reaction to take place, then the rate at which A and B are used up and the rate at which product is formed, in short, the rate of reaction is given by the expression

$$\text{Rate of reaction} \propto [A][B]$$

or

$$\text{Rate of reaction} = k_2 \; [A][B]$$

where k_2, the proportionality constant, is the rate when both concentrations are unity (say 1 mole/liter) and is, therefore, spoken of as the specific rate or, more generally, as the rate constant of the reaction. The subscript 2 in k_2 is used because this reaction involves two concentration terms. The reaction is spoken of as a second-order reaction or as one involving second-order kinetics. Thus the gas phase reaction

$$H_2 + I_2 \; \rightarrow \; 2 \, HI$$

is proportional both to the hydrogen and iodine concentrations

$$\text{Rate of formation of HI} = k_2[H_2][I_2]$$

where k_2 at 700° K is found to be 0.064 liter/mole sec, concentrations are expressed in moles per liter, and the rate is given as moles of HI formed per liter per second.

How then do we account for the fact that benzene is nitrated to form nitrobenzene at a rate independent of the benzene concentration? And how do we account for the further fact that some derivatives of benzene such as toluene (methyl benzene, $C_6H_5CH_3$) and ethyl benzene ($C_6H_5C_2H_5$) are nitrated at precisely the same rate as benzene? What chemists have done is to hold to their belief in the dependence of rate on concentration even in the apparent exceptions. They argue that the nitration must occur in stages; that the observed rate must be due to a slow stage not involving the benzene at all. It was largely due to this belief that the two-stage mechanism for the production of the $NO_2 ^{\oplus}$ ion was suggested—with the further provision that whereas the protonation step in Eq. (2-1) is fast, the fission of the $H_2NO_3^{\oplus}$ ion is the slow and "rate-determining" step.

$$HNO_3 + HNO_3 \xrightarrow{\text{fast}} H_2NO_3^{\oplus} + NO_3^{\ominus} \tag{2-1}$$

$$H_2NO_3^{\oplus} \xrightarrow{\text{slow}} H_2O + NO_2^{\oplus} \tag{2-2}$$

The subsequent nitration steps are again fast

$$NO_2^{\oplus} + C_6H_6 \xrightarrow{\text{fast}} C_6H_6NO_2^{\oplus} \tag{2-3}$$

$$C_6H_6NO_2^{\oplus} + B \xrightarrow{\text{fast}} C_6H_5NO_2 + BH^{\oplus} \tag{2-4}$$

where B is any base (proton acceptor).

Equation (2-2) is the bottleneck of the reaction. Benzene can only be nitrated at the rate at which $NO_2^{\oplus}$ is formed in Eq. (2-2). An analogy might be a mass production line producing automobiles. If car bodies are produced at 10 per hour and need to be fitted with tires to be completed, then no matter how large the supply of tires (as long as there are enough to equip at least 10 cars per hour) the rate of production of cars will also be 10 per hour. This explanation is sufficient to account for the identical rates of nitration of benzene, toluene, and ethylbenzene. The rate that is measured is that of the production of the nitronium ion, $NO_2^{\oplus}$.

Certain other substituted benzenes are sufficiently less reactive so that their reaction with $NO_2^{\oplus}$ in Eq. (2-3) is as slow as, or slower than, Eq. (2-2). Thus ethyl benzoate's rate law is

$$\text{Rate} \propto [C_6H_5CO_2C_2H_5]$$

The $CO_2C_2H_5$ group is a deactivating group significantly lowering the reactivity of the benzene ring.

In the conditions we have discussed so far, nitric acid has been in large excess, so that its concentration does not change measurably as the reaction proceeds. The amount of $NO_2^\oplus$ used up is a negligible part of the supply available from the nitric acid.

2-2 HALOGENATION OF KETONES [4a,5b]

A second, much-studied example of a reaction whose rate is independent of one of the chemicals being used up is the iodination of acetone.

$$\underset{\substack{\|\\O\\ \text{Acetone}}}{CH_3CCH_3} + I_2 \longrightarrow \underset{\substack{\|\\O\\ \text{Iodoacetone}}}{CH_3CCH_2I} + HI \qquad (2\text{-}5)$$

The rate of this reaction is independent of the concentration of iodine and again we conclude that there must be a slow bottleneck step preceding the reaction with iodine.

The reaction is catalyzed, that is, its rate is influenced by the bases present; the mechanism suggested is a slow removal of a proton from carbon by a base, followed by rapid reaction of the ion formed with iodine.

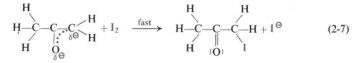

$$(2\text{-}6)$$

$$(2\text{-}7)$$

Resonance formulation of
anion formed in Eq. (2-6)

If the mechanism is correct, we should be able to replace I_2 by other reagents with no change in rate, and this is in fact the case. Reaction with bromine, Br_2, proceeds at the same rate as iodination (the product is CH_2COCH_2Br).

2-3 ALIPHATIC SUBSTITUTIONS [4*b*,5*c*,6*b*,9]

Occasionally research simplifies the scientist's picture of nature. What could possibly be the mechanism underlying the equation

$$2\ KMnO_4 \quad + \quad 5\ H_2S \quad + \quad 3\ H_2SO_4 \quad \longrightarrow$$

Potassium permanganate	Hydrogen sulfide	Sulfuric acid

$$5\ S \quad + \quad 2\ MnSO_4 \quad + \quad K_2SO_4 \quad + \quad 8\ H_2O \quad (2\text{-}8)$$

Sulfur	Manganous sulfate	Potassium sulfate	Water

The equation suggests that two molecules of potassium permanganate react with five hydrogen sulfide and three of sulfuric acid to yield the products. But is it plausible that 10 molecules collide simultaneously and rearrange into the product molecules? Calculations show that even the simultaneous collision of three bodies is so much rarer than that of two (by a factor of at least a thousand), that such three-center collisions would produce extremely slow reactions. Reactions involving 10-center collisions should be too slow to be measurable. Thus it becomes plausible that complicated equations are the result of several two-center reactions. We have already seen such a sequence of reactions, involving never more than two bodies at a time, in the nitration of benzene. Many organic reactions when studied in detail appear to be made up of simple reaction steps, one of the commonest of which is a substitution or displacement. In principle this can be of three kinds:

1. $A: + D(: E \rightarrow A : D + : E$ (Nucleophilic attack by A)

Reagent A, containing an unshared pair of electrons, competes with E: for its attachment to D. Here A's electrons seek a nucleus to which to bond. Hence A: is spoken of as a nucleophilic (nucleus-seeking) reagent. We will see numerous examples of this below.

2. $A + D:)E \rightarrow A : D + E$ (Electrophilic attack by A)

A again competes with E but in this case A needs E's bonding electrons and E is displaced without them. A is "electron-seeking" and is spoken of as an electrophilic reagent. An example is the $NO_2^{\oplus}$ ion in the nitration of benzene. The substitution liberates a proton (which is picked up by a base).

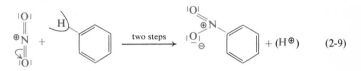

$$\text{(2-9)}$$

Most common substitutions of the benzene ring are caused by electrophilic reagents.

3. $A\cdot + D\overset{\cdot}{\underset{\cdot}{:}}E \rightarrow A:D + \cdot E$ (Free-radical attack by A)

In the third possibility, A is an atom or group carrying an unpaired electron. It is spoken of as a free-radical reagent. The product also carries an unpaired electron. Free radicals are significant in a number of polymer syntheses and also in some biological reactions.

At the moment we will concern ourselves with the first type of substitution, where the substituting agent brings its bonding electron pair with it and the leaving group departs with the electron pair by which it was bonded. There are numerous examples:

(*a*) *Alcohol formation from alkyl halides and hydroxide ion*

$$H\text{—}\overset{\ominus}{\underset{\cdot\cdot}{O}}\text{I} + CH_3\underset{\overline{}}{(}\text{—}\overline{Br}\text{I} \rightarrow H\text{—}\overline{O}\text{—}CH_3 + \text{I}\overline{\underset{\cdot\cdot}{Br}}\text{I}^{\ominus} \qquad \text{(2-10)}$$

| Hydroxide ion | Methyl bromide | Methanol | Bromide ion |

If sodium hydroxide, $Na^{\oplus}OH^{\ominus}$, is used as the nucleophilic reagent, sodium bromide, $Na^{\oplus}Br^{\ominus}$, will result. Note that the sodium ion is not involved in the reaction. *Alkyl halide* is the general term for a halogen-substituted saturated hydrocarbon, i.e., a hydrocarbon not containing double or triple bonds or benzene rings. Examples that we will be discussing are:

Hydrocarbon	Alkyl Halide

Methane
 	
H
  |
H—C—H
  |
H
	CH_3Cl (methyl chloride or chloromethane) [further chlorination gives CH_2Cl_2 (methylene dichloride or dichloromethane); $CHCl_3$ (chloroform); CCl_4 (carbon tetrachloride)]

Ethane H H | | H—C—C—H | | H H	C_2H_5Br (ethyl bromide or bromoethane)

Propane
 	
H H H
| | |
H—C—C—C—H
| | |
H H H
	$CH_3CH_2CH_2I$ (*n*-propyl iodide or 1-iodopropane); CH_3CHCH_3 (isopropyl bromide or 2-bromopropane)
	    |
	   Br

Butane or *n*-butane
 	
$CH_3CH_2CH_2CH_3$
	$CH_3CH_2CH_2CH_2Cl$ (*n*-butyl chloride or 1-chlorobutane); $CH_3CHCH_2CH_3$ (secondary or *sec*-butyl bromide or 2-bromobutane)
	    |
	   Br

Isobutane or 2-methylpropane
 	
CH_3—CH—CH_3
    |
   CH_3
	$(CH_3)_2CHCH_2I$ (isobutyl iodide or 1-iodo-2-methyl-propane);
	
	CH_3
	CH_3—C—I (tertiary or *tert*-butyl iodide or 2-iodo-2-
	CH_3 methylpropane)

(b) Hydrolysis of alkyl halides

Hydrolysis means breaking (*lysis*) by means of water. An alcohol is again formed. The overall reaction is $R—X + H_2O \rightarrow ROH + HX$, but the initial substitution follows scheme (1) above

$$H-\overset{\cdot\cdot}{\underset{H}{O}}| + R\overset{}{\underset{}{\subset}}X \longrightarrow H-\overset{\oplus}{\underset{H}{O}}-R + |X^{\ominus}$$

Protonated alcohol (2-11)

$$\downarrow H_2O$$

$$H-\overset{\cdot\cdot}{\underline{O}}-R + H_3O^{\oplus}$$
Alcohol

(c) Halogen exchange

$$|\overset{\ominus}{\underline{I}}| + \overset{CH_3}{\underset{|}{CH_2}}-Cl \xrightarrow[\text{solvent}]{\text{acetone}} |\overset{CH_3}{\underset{|}{\underline{I}}}-CH_2 + |\overset{\ominus}{\underline{Cl}}| \quad (2\text{-}12)$$

This reaction can be made to go quantitatively to the right by the use of sodium iodide because sodium iodide is appreciably soluble in acetone while the product, sodium chloride, is almost insoluble.

(d) Formation of nitriles (cyanides) and, hence, of carboxylic acids

$$|N\equiv C|^{\ominus} + \overset{CH_3}{\underset{|}{CH_2}}\overset{}{\underset{}{\subset}}\overline{Br}| \longrightarrow |N\equiv C-\overset{CH_3}{\underset{|}{CH_2}} + |\overset{\ominus}{\underline{Br}}| \quad (2\text{-}13)$$

Sodium cyanide or potassium cyanide is used and the reaction is useful for creating a new carbon—carbon bond, thus increasing the carbon-chain length by one unit. Treatment with reducing agents such as zinc and hydrochloric acid, lithium aluminum hydride (LiAlH$_4$) or sodium and alcohol converts the nitrile to the amine

$$C_2H_5C\equiv N \xrightarrow{4\,[H]} C_2H_5CH_2NH_2 \quad (2\text{-}14)$$

Propionitrile   *n*-Propylamine

Treatment of the nitrile with water (and acid or base to speed up the reaction) yields an organic acid

$$C_2H_5C\equiv N + 2\ H_2O \longrightarrow \underset{\underset{O}{\|}}{C_2H_5C}-OH\ +\ NH_3 \qquad (2\text{-}15)$$

Propionic Acid

(e) Hofmann synthesis of amines

$$H_3N\overset{..}{} + \underset{\underset{\underset{CH_2}{|}}{\overset{CH_3}{|}}}{CH_2}\left(-\bar{\underset{.}{B}}r\overset{..}{}\right) \longrightarrow H-\underset{\underset{H}{|}}{\overset{\overset{CH_3}{|}}{\overset{CH_2}{|}}}{\overset{H\quad CH_2}{\underset{\oplus}{N}}}-CH_2\ +\ \overset{..}{}\bar{\underset{.}{B}}r\overset{..}{}{}^{\ominus} \qquad (2\text{-}16)$$

$$\Big\downarrow NH_3$$

$$H_2N-C_3H_7 + NH_4^{\oplus}$$

n-Propylamine

Amines can participate in this reaction sequence since they too contain an unshared electron pair

$$CH_3CH_2CH_2\overset{..}{N}\Big\langle{\overset{H}{\underset{H}{}}}\ +\ CH_3\Big(-Br \longrightarrow$$

$$CH_3CH_2CH_2-\underset{\underset{H}{|}}{\overset{\overset{\textstyle\diagup H\diagdown}{}}{\underset{\oplus}{N}}}-CH_3 \xrightarrow{\ NH_3\ } CH_3CH_2CH_2\overset{..}{N}\Big\langle{\overset{CH_3}{\underset{H}{}}}\ +\ \overset{\oplus}{N}H_4 \qquad (2\text{-}17)$$

$$+\ Br^{\ominus} \qquad\qquad \text{Methyl-}n\text{-propylamine}$$

$$\underset{\underset{CH_3}{\diagup}}{\overset{\overset{CH_3CH_2CH_2}{\diagdown}}{H-\overset{..}{N}}}\ +\ CH_3\Big(-Br \longrightarrow \underset{\underset{CH_3}{|}}{\overset{\overset{CH_3CH_2CH_2}{|}}{H-\overset{\oplus}{N}}}-CH_3 \longrightarrow$$

Methyl-*n*-propylamine

$$+\ Br^{\ominus}$$

$$\underset{\underset{CH_3}{\diagdown}}{\overset{\overset{CH_2CH_2CH_3}{\diagup}}{\overset{..}{N}-CH_3}}\ +\quad H^{\oplus} \qquad (2\text{-}18)$$

Dimethyl-*n*-propylamine

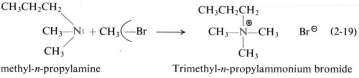

Dimethyl-*n*-propylamine   Trimethyl-*n*-propylammonium bromide

The last product is an alkyl-substituted ammonium bromide ($NH_4^{\oplus}Br^{\ominus}$) and is called a *quaternary ammonium salt.*

The simple amino group, NH_2, is a constituent of many amino acids. Some of these acids are made from halogen acids by the type of nucleophilic substitution we have discussed.

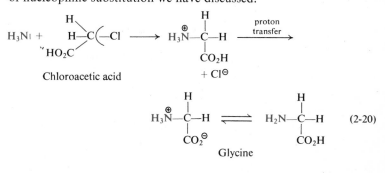

Chloroacetic acid

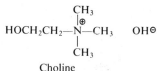

Glycine

A quaternary ammonium compound, choline, is found in muscle tissue

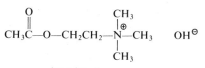

Choline

and its derivative, acetylcholine

$$CH_3\overset{O}{\overset{\|}{C}}-O-CH_2CH_2-\underset{\underset{CH_3}{|}}{\overset{\overset{CH_3}{|}}{\overset{\oplus}{N}}}-CH_3 \quad OH^{\ominus}$$

Acetylcholine

plays an integral part in the transmission of nerve impulses across synapses.

(f) Ether synthesis

If an alcohol is treated with sodium, a sodium salt is obtained whose anion often acts as a powerful nucleophilic agent

$$2\,C_2H_5OH + 2\,Na \rightarrow 2\,C_2H_5\overset{\ominus}{O}\,\overset{\oplus}{Na} + H_2 \tag{2-21}$$

Sodium
ethoxide

Thus the anesthetic ether or diethyl ether may be prepared.

$$C_2H_5\overset{\ominus}{\underline{O}}\vert \quad + \; C_2H_5\!\!\left(\!-Br \rightarrow C_2H_5\underline{O}\!-\!C_2H_5 + Br^{\ominus}\right.$$
$$Na^{\oplus} \hspace{6.5cm} Na^{\oplus} \tag{2-22}$$

Sodium ethoxide   Diethyl ether

Unsymmetrical ethers may also be prepared by this method

$$C_2H_5\overset{\ominus}{\underline{O}}\vert + CH_3\!\!\left(\!-Br \longrightarrow \; C_2H_5\underline{O}\!-\!CH_3 \; + \; Br^{\ominus}\right.$$
$$Na^{\oplus} \hspace{6.5cm} Na^{\oplus} \tag{2-23}$$

Ethyl methyl ether

(g) Synthesis of sulfur compounds

Since sulfur is also in Group VI of the periodic table we might expect it to follow some of the oxygen reactions. Thus the thiol group, SH, a constituent of the amino acid cysteine

$$HSCH_2\overset{\displaystyle|}{\underset{\underset{\oplus}{NH_3}}{C}}HCO_2^{\ominus}$$

can be introduced into organic compounds by use of the ion, $SH^{\ominus}$

$$H_2S \hspace{1.5cm} + \; NaOH \rightarrow Na^{\oplus}HS^{\ominus} + H_2O \tag{2-24}$$

Hydrogen sulfide   Sodium
(a weak acid)   hydrosulfide

$$H\underline{S}\vert^{\ominus} + CH_3\!\!\left(\!-Br \rightarrow \; H\underline{S}\!-\!CH_3 \; + \; Br^{\ominus}\right. \tag{2-25}$$

Methanethiol

The thiols are still weak acids and can be neutralized with bases, making possible a simple synthesis of thioethers

$$CH_3SH + NaOH \rightarrow CH_3S^\ominus Na^\oplus + H_2O \qquad (2\text{-}26)$$

$$CH_3S^\ominus + C_2H_5{-}Br \rightarrow CH_3S{-}C_2H_5 + Br^\ominus \qquad (2\text{-}27)$$

Ethyl methyl
thioether

One peculiarity of thiol groups is their easy oxidation by air, iodine, or biological oxidizing agents to disulfides

$$2\ C_2H_5SH \xrightarrow{[o]} C_2H_5{-}S{-}S{-}C_2H_5 + H_2O \qquad (2\text{-}28)$$

Diethyl disulfide

In this way two cysteine residues in proteins are often found linked together by an S—S bridge.

(*h*) *Phosphorus compounds*

If we replace NH_3 by phosphine, PH_3, we can obtain the corresponding alkyl phosphines

$$\bar{P}H_3 + 3\ CH_3{-}I \xrightarrow{\text{3 steps}} P(CH_3)_3 + 3\ HI \qquad (2\text{-}29)$$

(*i*) *Alkylation of malonic esters*

Even some very complex syntheses often contain substitution steps. Thus malonic acid, $CH_2(CO_2H)_2$, can be converted to its ethyl ester, $CH_2(CO_2C_2H_5)_2$, and to its sodium salt, $Na^\oplus \ \overset{\ominus}{C}H(CO_2CH_5)_2$. The anion of this salt can react with alkyl halides

$$\underset{\overset{|}{CO_2C_2H_5}}{\overset{\overset{CO_2C_2H_5}{|}}{H{-}\underset{}{C}^\ominus}} + CH_3{-}\bar{B}r \longrightarrow \underset{\overset{|}{CO_2C_2H_5}}{\overset{\overset{CO_2C_2H_5}{|}}{H{-}\underset{}{C}{-}CH_3}} + \bar{B}r^\ominus \qquad (2\text{-}30)$$

Diethyl ester of
2-methylmalonic acid

2-4   THE REACTION OF ALKYL HALIDES WITH HYDROXIDE ION AND WATER [5a,6b,8]

If we substitute the hydrogens in methyl bromide successively by methyl groups (CH_3)

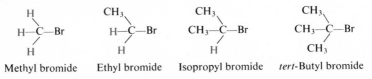

Methyl bromide   Ethyl bromide   Isopropyl bromide   *tert*-Butyl bromide

and measure the rates of their reaction with hydroxide ion, we find a most surprising result. The first insertion of a methyl group slows down the rate, the second has very little effect, and the third greatly speeds it up. The relationship is shown in Fig. 2-3.

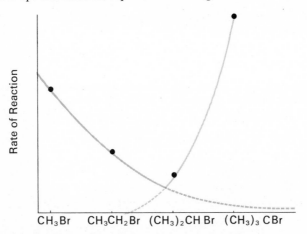

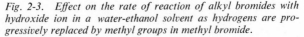

Fig. 2-3.   Effect on the rate of reaction of alkyl bromides with hydroxide ion in a water-ethanol solvent as hydrogens are progressively replaced by methyl groups in methyl bromide.

One of the surest signs that more than one factor is operating in a system is the discovery that doing the same thing systematically, over and over again, first has one effect and then the opposite. In the present instance one suspects that the insertion of methyl groups lowers the tendency of the alkyl halide to react by one path, but enhances the possibility of an alternative mechanism which eventually dominates. To support this viewpoint it was discovered that the rate of the CH_3Br reaction follows the equation

$$Rate = k_2[CH_3Br][OH^{\ominus}]$$

while the *tert*-butyl bromide rate is independent of the $OH^{\ominus}$ concentration

$$Rate = k_1[(CH_3)_3CBr]$$

Doubling the $OH^{\ominus}$ concentration (while temperature and other concentrations are unchanged) has no effect on the rate.

The CH_3Br reaction is generally accepted as a simple attack by the nucleophilic reagent $OH^{\ominus}$ on the carbon of CH_3Br, going through a transition state in which oxygen is partially attached to carbon and the C—Br bond is weakened

$$(2\text{-}31)$$

In the *tert*-butyl bromide reaction we again assume that the lack of dependence of rate on one of the reagents implies a slow step not involving that reagent and we formulate it as an ionization

$$(CH_3)_3C\left(-\bar{\underline{Br}}\right) \xrightarrow{\text{slow}} (CH_3)_3C^{\oplus} + \text{ } \bar{\underline{Br}}^{\ominus} \qquad (2\text{-}32)$$

The *tert*-butyl cation then reacts rapidly with solvent molecules or $OH^{\ominus}$ ions in its vicinity

$$(CH_3)_3C^{\oplus} \xrightarrow[\text{fast}]{2\ H_2O} (CH_3)_3COH + H_3O^{\oplus} \qquad (2\text{-}33)$$

$$(CH_3)_3C^{\oplus} \xrightarrow[\text{fast}]{OH^{\ominus}} (CH_3)_3COH \qquad (2\text{-}34)$$

It might be argued that $(CH_3)_3CBr$ reacts with water rather than $OH^{\ominus}$ by a one-step process similar to the $CH_3Br\cdots OH^{\ominus}$ reaction. Since water is in excess, the rate of reaction would not be noticeably dependent on it; the water concentration would be essentially constant throughout the reaction. However, this alternative is unlikely since $OH^{\ominus}$ is so much more powerful a base and nucleophilic reagent than water.

To check on the ionization mechanism as a possible path for alkyl halide and similar reactions, a number of tests have been run. (*a*) Certain displacement reactions yield different products at identical rates. Thus *tert*-butyl chloride reacts with water in formic acid, HCO_2H, to form *tert*-butyl alcohol

$$(CH_3)_3C\text{—}Br + 2\,H_2O \rightarrow (CH_3)_3COH + H_3O^{\oplus} + {}_{|}Br^{\ominus} \qquad (2\text{-}35)$$

When calcium formate, $Ca(HCO_2)_2$, is added, a significant amount of *tert*-butyl formate is produced, but the rate is not changed. Similarly, the addition of calcium chloroacetate, $Ca(ClCH_2CO_2)_2$, yields *tert*-butyl chloroacetate, $ClCH_2CO_2C(CH_3)_3$, without any change in rate. These findings are most easily explained if we assume the formation of the *tert*-butyl cation in the slow step followed by rapid reaction of the cation with water, formate, or chloroacetate ion.

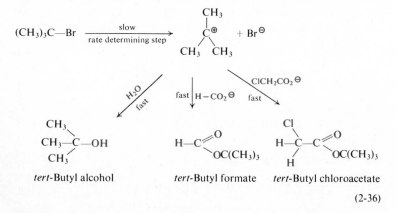

$$(2\text{-}36)$$

It might be objected that an alternative mechanism could explain the data equally well. The alcohol might be formed first in all cases, followed by fast reaction of the latter with formate or chloroacetate

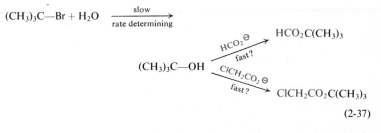

$$(2\text{-}37)$$

This proposal can be tested. If the first product, $(CH_3)_3COH$, is treated with formate or chloroacetate ion, the reaction is found to be slower than the rate of formation of the alcohol. Thus the alternate mechanism would give different rates with and without the added ions, contrary to the evidence. The ionization mechanism, therefore, remains the most plausible.

(*b*) Even in the absence of water certain substitutions proceed at a rate independent of the concentration of the nucleophilic reagent. Thus *tert*-butyl bromide exchanges bromide ion in liquid sulfur dioxide solvent at a rate independent of the $Br^\ominus$ concentration. To detect exchange, radioactive $Br^{*\ominus}$ is used

$$(CH_3)_3CBr + Br^{*\ominus} \rightleftharpoons (CH_3)_3CBr^* + Br^\ominus \qquad (2\text{-}38)$$

This must again imply that the slow step is the ionization of *tert*-butyl bromide and does not involve attack by bromide ion.

(*c*) If two different alkyl halides form the same intermediate, what follows this stage should be identical. Diphenylmethyl chloride and diphenylmethyl bromide produce the same percentage of diphenyl-carbinol and diphenylmethyl azide when reacting in an aqueous solvent with azide ion, $N_3^\ominus$,

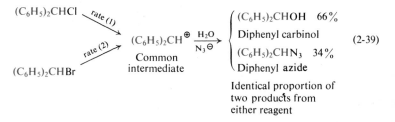

(*d*) Conditions for the preparation of stable carbonium salts: Just as the postulation of the nitronium ion as an intermediate led to the isolation of stable salts of the $NO_2^\oplus$ cation, so a search for salts of substituted methyl cations followed the postulation of the ionization mechanism for alkyl halides. At an early stage, freezing-point measurements of triphenyl carbinol in sulfuric acid were found to give a fourfold freezing-point depression ascribed to the ionization

$$(C_6H_5)_3COH + 2\,H_2SO_4 \rightarrow (C_6H_5)_3C^\oplus + H_3O^\oplus + 2\,HSO_4^\ominus \qquad (2\text{-}40)$$

A yellow solution is obtained with the same spectrum in the visible and ultraviolet region as that of $(C_6H_5)_3CCl$ in liquid sulfur dioxide where the ionization almost certainly produces $(C_6H_5)_3C^\oplus$ ions

$$(C_6H_5)_3CCl \xrightarrow{\text{SO}_2 \text{ solvent}} (C_6H_5)_3C^\oplus + Cl^\ominus \qquad (2\text{-}41)$$

More recently Olah (Case–Western Reserve) has developed evidence for a number of stable carbonium salts in solution. When alkyl fluorides are added to antimony fluoride, SbF_5, a solvent with strong affinity for fluoride ion, the alkyl fluorides dissolve and the solutions spectroscopically give evidence of stable carbonium ions in a number of cases. Nuclear magnetic resonance, which can distinguish protons located in different environments, gives only one strong peak when *n*-butyl fluoride, isobutyl fluoride, and *tert*-butyl fluoride are dissolved in SbF_5. The single peak, at a position on the spectrum far removed

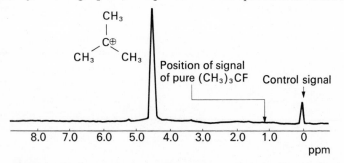

Fig. 2-4. *Nuclear magnetic resonance spectrum of tert-butyl cation from the butyl fluorides in excess* SbF_5. [*After G. A. Olah and C. U. Pittman, Jr., Advances in Phys. Org. Chem.,* **4**: 305(1966).]

from that obtained from pure *tert*-butyl fluoride, must correspond to the *tert*-butyl cation. The *n*-butyl and isobutyl groups contain CH_2 as well as CH_3 groups and would give a much more complex spectrum. The last two groups must rearrange to form the *tert*-butyl cation:

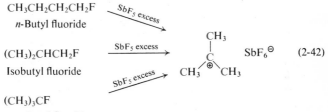

$$CH_3CH_2CH_2CH_2F \xrightarrow{SbF_5 \ excess}$$
n-Butyl fluoride

$$(CH_3)_2CHCH_2F \xrightarrow{SbF_5 \ excess}$$
Isobutyl fluoride

$$(CH_3)_3CF$$
tert-Butyl fluoride

(2-42)

Seven isomeric pentyl fluorides give the same *tert*-pentyl cation:

$$C_5H_{11}F \xrightarrow{excess \ SbF_5} CH_3CH_2C^{\oplus} \overset{CH_3}{\underset{CH_3}{\big\langle}} + SbF_6^{\ominus} \quad (2\text{-}43)$$

The *tert*-butyl cation is obtained from the two isomeric butanes by dissolving them in fluorosulfonic acid and SbF_5. At $-60°C$ crystalline salts are isolated

$$(CH_3)_3CH \xrightarrow{excess \ FSO_3H-SbF_5} (CH_3)_3C^{\oplus}SbF_5FSO_3^{\ominus} + H_2 \quad (2\text{-}44)$$
(or $CH_3CH_2CH_2CH_3$)

whose nuclear magnetic resonance spectrum in liquid sulfur dioxide is that of the *tert*-butyl cation. These experiments indicate the considerable stability of the *tert*-carbonium ion and thus support the view that *tert*-alkyl halides do indeed often react through the intermediary of the carbonium ion.

2-5 THE MEASUREMENT OF REACTION RATES [2,7]

We have spoken several times of certain rates being proportional to the concentration of one or more of the reagents. But concentrations change as the reaction proceeds. Fig. 2-5 shows concentration changes

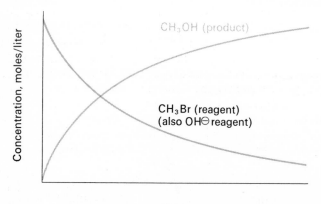

Fig. 2-5. Change of concentration of reagents and product with time in reaction $CH_3Br + OH^\ominus \rightarrow CH_3OH + Br^\ominus$.

in a simple one-stage displacement reaction. If the rate is proportional to the concentration of a reagent whose concentration is decreasing, the rate also should decrease and this is in fact found. How, then, do we obtain a numerical value for the rate and study its dependence on concentration? The simplest method in principle is to measure reaction rates under initial (known) conditions before significant changes in concentration have taken place. Doing this at several different initial concentrations will indicate the change in rate with concentration. Thus we might follow the reaction

$$(CH_3)_3CBr + OH^\ominus \xrightarrow[\text{solvent}]{\text{acetone–water}} (CH_3)_3COH + Br^\ominus$$

by seeing how much $OH^\ominus$ disappears in the first few minutes of reaction (by titration with acid) or by seeing how much $Br^\ominus$ has been formed (by potentiometric titration with $Ag^\oplus$). The experiment is then repeated with double the initial concentration of $OH^\ominus$, and then with double the $(CH_3)_3CBr$ concentration. The first doubling does not affect the rate, the second does. We, therefore, write

$$\text{Rate} = k_1[(CH_3)_3CBr]$$

With methyl bromide, CH_3Br, both doublings will double the rate so that

$$\text{Rate} = k_2[CH_3Br][OH^\ominus]$$

One problem is to stop the reaction after a short time and keep it from reacting while it is being analyzed. In the above reactions this can be done by cooling the reaction mixture with ice which greatly slows down the rate, by adding a solvent (such as excess acetone) in which the reaction is much slower, or by adding a solvent such as carbon tetrachloride which separates the reagents, extracting the alkyl halide which dissolves in CCl_4 while the $OH^\ominus$ remains in the aqueous layer.

A more sophisticated procedure allows the calculation of the rate constant throughout the reaction process in spite of variations in concentration.

Suppose in a reaction step, $A + B \rightarrow$ products

$$\text{Rate} = k_2[A][B]$$

we can express the rate during a small time interval Δt, as the change of concentration of A (i.e., $\Delta[A]$) or of B (i.e., $\Delta[B]$) during this interval. Since these concentrations decrease while the rate is a positive quantity, we write

$$\frac{-\Delta[A]}{\Delta t} = \frac{-\Delta[B]}{\Delta t} = k_2[A][B] \qquad (2\text{-}45)$$

For accuracy we should make the time interval as small as possible, and, in the limit of the infinitesimally small, we write Δt as dt and ΔA as dA, etc.

$$\frac{-dA}{dt} = \frac{-dB}{dt} = k_2[A][B] \qquad (2\text{-}46)$$

Note

$$\frac{-dA}{dt} = \frac{-dB}{dt}$$

only when one molecule of A reacts with one of B. If the rate-determining step of a reaction were $A + 2B \rightarrow$ products, then B will disappear twice as fast as A and

$$\frac{-dA}{dt} = \frac{-1}{2}\frac{dB}{dt} = k_3[A][B]^2 \qquad (2\text{-}47)$$

We can handle the equation

$$\frac{-d\text{A}}{dt} = k_2[\text{A}][\text{B}]$$

by the methods of the calculus. Suppose we begin with the initial concentration of both A and B equal at a moles per liter. At time t let x moles per liter have reacted, so that $[\text{A}] = [\text{B}] = a - x$.

Thus

$$\frac{-d(a - x)}{dt} = k_2(a - x)^2 \tag{2-48}$$

But

$$\frac{-d(a - x)}{dt} = \frac{dx}{dt}$$

since the rate of loss of material present initially equals the rate of material reacted. Mathematically we can say

$$\frac{-d(a - x)}{dt} = \frac{-da}{dt} + \frac{dx}{dt} = \frac{dx}{dt}$$

since a is a constant and, therefore, its rate of change with time is zero. Hence

$$\frac{dx}{dt} = k_2(a - x)^2 \tag{2-49}$$

or

$$\frac{dx}{(a - x)^2} = k_2 \, dt \tag{2-50}$$

If this is integrated we obtain

$$\frac{-1}{a - x} = k_2 t + C$$

where C is a constant. Evaluating C, which must be the same at all values of x and t, we know that when $t = 0$, $x = 0$, and therefore, $-1/a = C$. Our equation finally becomes

$$\frac{-1}{a - x} = k_2 t - \frac{1}{a} \tag{2-51}$$

or

$$k_2 t = \frac{1}{a - x} - \frac{1}{a} \tag{2-52}$$

Thus for a reaction whose rate is proportional to two concentration terms both with initial concentration a, substituting values of x and t throughout the reaction should give always the same value for k_2

$$k_2 = \frac{1}{t}\left(\frac{1}{a-x} - \frac{1}{a}\right) \tag{2-53}$$

If initial concentrations are not equal, we write

$$\frac{dx}{dt} = k_2(a-x)(b-x) \tag{2-54}$$

which on integrating gives

$$k_2 = \frac{1}{(a-b)t}\ln\frac{b(a-x)}{a(b-x)} \tag{2-55}$$

where ln signifies use of natural logarithms; or, using logarithms to base 10,

$$k_2 = \frac{2.303}{(a-b)t}\log\frac{b(a-x)}{a(b-x)} \tag{2-56}$$

For the ionization mechanism

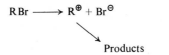

$$\frac{dx}{dt} = k_1(a-x) \tag{2-57}$$

where a is the initial concentration of RBr.

When this is integrated

$$k_1 = \frac{2.303}{t}\log\frac{a}{a-x} \tag{2-58}$$

or

$$\frac{k_1 t}{2.303} = \log a - \log(a-x) \tag{2-59}$$

Two tests can be made of this equation. In one we can plot log $(a-x)$, that is, log [A], against t. A straight line should be obtained of slope $-k_1/2.303$. This is done in Fig. 2-6 for the reaction of $0.1028M$ $(CH_3)_3CBr$ in 60% dioxane–

40% water by volume, at 10.00°C. Samples of 5-ml volume were taken out of a 100-ml reaction flask at various recorded times and transferred into excess acetone at 0°C to stop the reaction. Titration with base showed the extent of the reaction

$$(CH_3)_3CBr + 2 H_2O \rightarrow (CH_3)_3COH + Br^\ominus + H_3O^\oplus$$

by reacting with the product $H_3O^\oplus$.

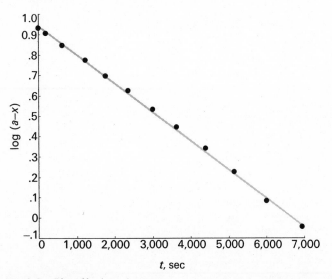

Fig. 2-6. Plot of $\log(a - x)$ against time, t, for the $(CH_3)_3CBr$ reaction in 60% dioxane–40% water at 10°C.

The points fall approximately on a straight line indicating that the reaction is a first-order reaction, that the rate is proportional to the concentration of only one reactant. From the slope of the best straight line, $k_1/2.303 = 1.42 \times 10^{-4}$, and hence, $k_1 = 32.7 \times 10^{-5}$.

The second test is to substitute values of x, a, and t into Eq. (2-58) and to evaluate k_1 for each point. The first-order rate constants (k_1) are seen to increase slightly, but not enough to make a second-order rate expression a better fit. (Rate constants calculated according to the second-order rate law [Eq. (2-53)] are given in the last column.)

Table 2-2 *tert*-**Butyl Bromide Hydrolysis in 60% Dioxane–40% Water at 10.00°C**
(Initial concentration $(CH_3)_3CBr = 0.1028M$. $(a - x)$ expressed in ml of $0.05958M$ NaOH per 5.02 ml sample.)

t sec	$(a-x)$ ml	k_1/sec	% Reaction	k_2 liters/mole sec [calculated from Eq. (2-53)]
0	8.66 ($= a$)			
210	8.15	28.9×10^{-5}	6	28.8×10^{-4}
630	7.20	29.3×10^{-5}	17	31.3×10^{-4}
1185	6.05	30.3×10^{-5}	30	35.4×10^{-4}
1790	5.01	30.6×10^{-5}	42	39.6×10^{-4}
2320	4.22	31.0×10^{-5}	51	44.1×10^{-4}
2995	3.39	31.3×10^{-5}	61	50.5×10^{-4}
3605	2.77	31.6×10^{-5}	68	57.4×10^{-4}
4350	2.19	31.6×10^{-5}	75	66.1×10^{-4}
5150	1.69	31.7×10^{-5}	80	77.9×10^{-4}
6005	1.24	32.4×10^{-5}	86	96.9×10^{-4}
6930	0.92	32.4×10^{-5}	89	118×10^{-4}

The small rise in first-order rate constant is ascribed to the $Br^{\ominus}$ and $H_3O^{\oplus}$ ions produced in the reaction since ions are known to facilitate the formation of alkyl cations. Added $Na^{\oplus}Br^{\ominus}$ or $H_3O^{\oplus}Br^{\ominus}$ produce about the same increase in rate. Figure 2-7 shows a plot of the rate constants, k_1 and k_2, against percent reaction. The lack of constancy of k_2 values demonstrates that the reaction did not follow a second-order rate law. From the first-order rate constants in Fig. 2-7 an initial rate constant of 28.9×10^{-5}/sec is obtained. A parallel run in the presence of $0.1M$ NaOH gave very similar data with an initial rate constant of 28.7×10^{-5}/sec, thus demonstrating the lack of interference of $OH^{\ominus}$ in the reaction.

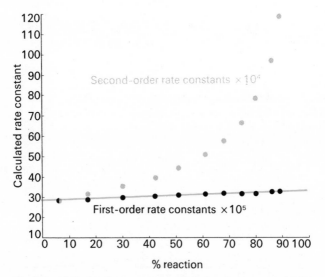

Fig. 2-7. Calculated rate constants plotted against percent reaction, in hydrolysis of tert-butyl bromide.
   × *Rate constants calculated from first-order rate equation.*
   + *Rate constants calculated from second-order rate equation.*
Approximate constancy of first-order rate constants indicates that reaction followed first-order rate law.

Instead of titrating samples of the reaction mixture from time to time, numerous other methods have been developed for following reactions. Some of these are "nondestructive" in the sense that they do not interfere with the reagents. Any property can be followed that is related in a known way to the concentration of at least one of the reagents. We have already discussed total volume measurements in the nitration process. Other properties that have been used are total pressure (in the case of gas reactions), spectroscopic absorption (following the decrease or increase in absorption at a given wavelength corresponding to one of the reagents or products), and refractive index.

SUGGESTED READINGS

1. Frost, A. A.: Effect of Concentration on Reaction Rate and Equilibrium, *J. Chem. Educ.*, **18**:272(1941).
2. Frost, A. A., and R. G. Pearson: "Kinetics and Mechanisms," 2d ed., John Wiley & Sons, Inc., New York, 1961.
3. Gould, E. S.: "Mechanism and Structure in Organic Chemistry," Henry Holt and Co., New York, 1959.
4. Hammett, L. P.: "Physical Organic Chemistry," chaps. 4 and 5, McGraw-Hill Book Company, New York, 1940.
5. Hine, J.: "Physical Organic Chemistry," 2d ed., (*a*) chaps. 2, 7; (*b*) chaps. 5, 10; (*c*) chaps. 6, 7, McGraw-Hill Book Company, New York, 1962.
6. Ingold, C. K.: "Structure and Mechanism in Organic Chemistry," (*a*) chap. 6; (*b*) chap. 7, Cornell University Press, Ithaca, N.Y., 1953.
7. Laidler, K. J.: "Chemical Kinetics," 2d ed., McGraw-Hill Book Company, New York, 1965.
8. Olah, G. A., and C. U. Pittman, Jr.: Spectroscopic Observation of Alkylcarbonium Ions in Strong Acid Solutions, *Advances in Phys. Org. Chem.*, **4**:305(1966).
9. Streitwieser, A.: "Solvolytic Displacement Reactions," McGraw-Hill Book Company, New York, 1962.

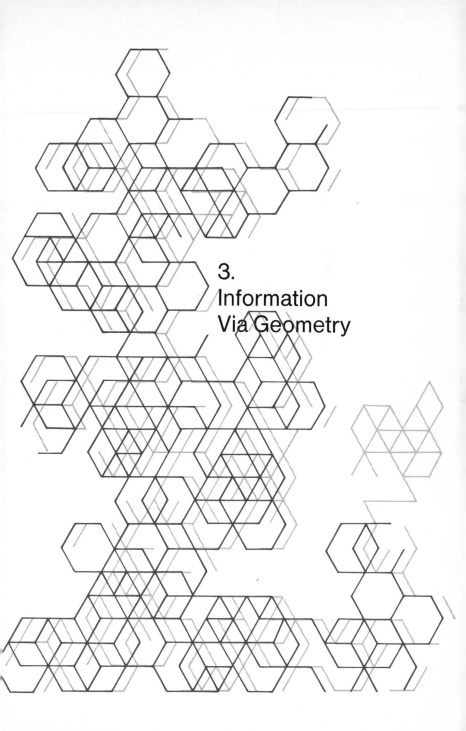

3.
Information
Via Geometry

3-1   INTRODUCTION   [1,4,8,11]

The original structural theory of organic chemistry was based on a "rubber-sheet geometry," no one thinking that atoms in a molecule would hold their precise relative positions in space. Although Couper began to write lines between atoms in 1858, they were not intended to indicate direction, only links.

The three formulas

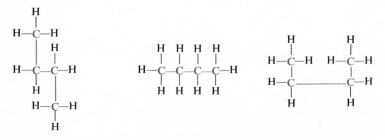

represent the same chemical, *n*-butane; they are "topologically" identical. If you drew them on a thin rubber sheet, you could twist each diagram till it was like the others. The scheme worked well. For numerous compounds one topologically distinct formula corresponded to one compound in nature. But there are a few exceptions. The anomalies covered by resonance theory we have already discussed. In that case more distinct formulas exist than compounds corresponding to them. But the converse anomaly exists also—more than one compound in nature corresponding to a single topological formula.

Lactic acid has the formula $CH_3CH(OH)CO_2H$. It can be isolated from sour milk and has a melting point of 53°C. A lactic acid with topologically the same formula can be isolated from muscle; we can feel it being produced when our muscles ache from overexertion. Its melting point is also 53°C. One would think from numerous tests that they are identical. One final test is often carried out to prove identity, the mixed melting point. Two samples of the same material when mixed should not affect any chemical or physical property (other than shape or mass). A sample that is not identical with a second sample, on the other hand, would interfere with the ordered arrangement of the second sample when mixed with it, and the observed result is a lowered melting point when small quantities of the first sample are introduced. The addition of more of the first sample may lead to the further lowering of the melting point or to an increase. Typical melting-point patterns when mixing substances of topologically identical formulas are shown in Fig. 3-1.

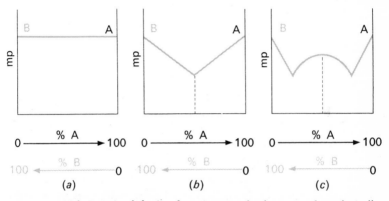

Fig. 3-1. *Melting point behavior for mixtures of substances of topologically identical formulas. If the behavior follows pattern (a), one concludes that A and B are identical; if (b) or (c) is followed, the two substances are different in some way.*

On mixing the lactic acids from sour milk and muscle, diagram (b) results. The two lactic acids must be different in some respect and the proposal was made in the 1860s and 1870s that the difference was likely to be a difference in the arrangement of the atoms of the molecule in space. A survey showed that the strange mixed-melting-point behavior was always found when the molecule contained a carbon atom to which four different atoms or groups were attached. Such a carbon atom is usually spoken of as an asymmetric carbon atom. When only three of the four were different, as in $CH_3CH_2CO_2H$, no melting point lowering was observed. In 1874 J. H. van't Hoff and J. A. leBel argued that a tetrahedral arrangement around carbon would demand two different molecules, $Cabcd$, where a, b, c, and d are different atoms or groups, whereas molecules Ca_2bc, Ca_3b, or Ca_4 could only exist in one arrangement.

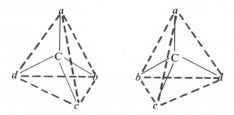

The two distinct tetrahedral structures C*abcd* are nonsuperimposable mirror images. The two lactic acids were, therefore, assigned the structures

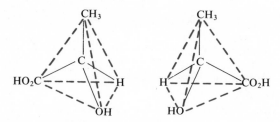

Attempts to make lactic acid in the laboratory produced a seemingly further distinct substance

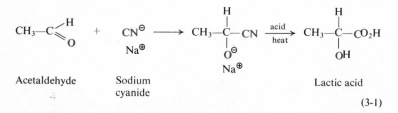

(3-1)

This synthetic lactic acid melted at 17°C and lowered the melting point of each of the earlier samples, but its own melting point was raised by them.

Careful examination showed that Fig. 3-2 corresponded to exactly half of Fig. 3-1*b*, suggesting that synthetic lactic acid was a 50/50 mixture of the two natural acids. This mixture is in fact to be expected on the tetrahedral hypothesis if we study the method of

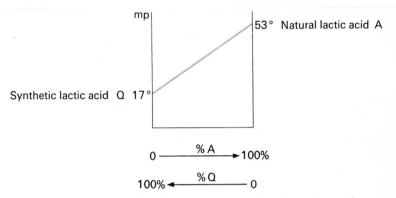

Fig. 3-2. *Melting-point behaviour of mixtures of synthetic and natural lactic acids.*

synthesis. Acetaldehyde is a planar structure according to this model, that is, the atoms

are all in one plane, if we consider the doubly bound oxygen as linked to two corners of the central carbon's tetrahedron. Now,

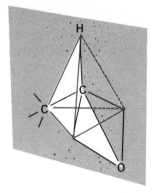

Fig. 3-3. *Planar relation of atoms in acetaldehyde.*

CN$^\ominus$ can attack on either side of the molecular plane, thereby yielding two different products of identical topological formula.

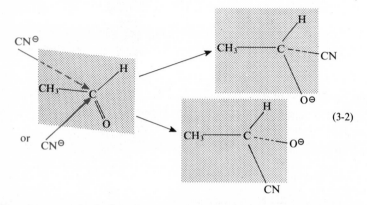

(3-2)

When these are hydrolyzed to lactic acid, the two forms found in nature are produced.

Since in normal reactions there are of the order of 10^{24} CN$^\ominus$ ions present, and since there is no reason why one side of the acetaldehyde molecules should be preferred for attack over the other, a 50/50 mixture can be expected. Such a mixture of mirror-image forms can be separated into its two components by one or more of the following methods:

(*a*) Sometimes the crystals of the two forms are mirror images of each other. They can then be separated by careful observation and selection under the microscope.

(*b*) The two forms react at different speeds with a nonplanar, non-symmetrical base, i.e., one which also has a topologically equivalent yet distinct partner such as quinine or codeine or 2-amino-butane,

$$
\begin{array}{c}
NH_2 \\
| \\
CH_3CCH_2CH_3 \\
| \\
H
\end{array}
$$

In this case the two acids do not behave in an equivalent way and one acid is preferred over the other, just as a right hand fits better into a right glove than a left hand does.

(*c*) Certain microorganisms will consume one form because it can make use of it in its metabolism but will leave the other. Here we have a hint that organisms are not symmetrical—something that has been amply confirmed.

3-2   OPTICAL ROTATION [4,8,9]

A characteristic and convenient property of the two forms of natural lactic acid is that they will rotate the plane of plane-polarized light to the same extent, but in opposite directions. If we think of ordinary light as vibrating in all directions, then certain materials such as a

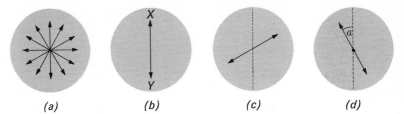

(a)	*(b)*	*(c)*	*(d)*

Fig. 3-4.   (a) Viewing ordinary light as it approaches the observer, its vibrations are in all directions. (b) Plane-polarized light vibrating in the XY plane. (c) Plane-polarized light rotated from its direction in (b), in a clockwise (+) direction. (d) Counterclockwise (−) rotation by α°.

sheet polarizer or a Nicol prism (Iceland Spar, $CaCO_3$, cut and cemented in a particular way) allow only vibrations in one direction to come through. The emerging light is spoken of as being plane-polarized. A second Nicol prism or sheet polarizer oriented in the same way as the first will let all light through. When at 90° to the first, no light will come through. When a solution of lactic acid from sour milk is placed between the two sheets, the second sheet no longer is held in a parallel orientation to the first for maximum light transmission, but must be rotated in a counterclockwise direction (relative to the observer). Lactic acid from muscle at the same concentration requires rotation to the same extent, but in a clockwise direction. Synthetic lactic acid is optically inactive. It requires no rotation of the second sheet polarizer. Lactic acid from milk is spoken of as levorotatory or as (−)-lactic acid, that from muscle as dextrorotatory or as (+)-lactic acid.

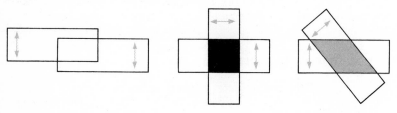

Fig. 3-5. The amount of light transmitted through a pair of sheet polarizers depends on their relative orientation.

The rotation observed at a given temperature using a given wavelength of light depends on length of light path through the solution and on concentration of the material.

$$\alpha = [\alpha]_\lambda^t \frac{l \times c}{10}$$

where α is the *observed rotation* in degrees, $[\alpha]_\lambda^t$ is the *specific rotation* of the substance at temperature t and wavelength λ, l is the length of solution in centimeters, and c is the concentration of solute in grams per milliliter of solvent. Thus $[\alpha]_\lambda^t$ is the observed rotation when plane-polarized light travels through 10 cm of solution containing 1 g solute per milliliter of solvent. The specific rotation for lactic acid from milk at room temperature using yellow light from a sodium vapor lamp is −3.8°, for lactic acid from muscle +3.8°, and for synthetic lactic acid 0. Synthetic lactic acid is spoken of as a *racemic mixture* and any process by which the (+) or (−) form is converted into a racemic mixture is called *racemization*.

3-3 STEREOCHEMISTRY OF NUCLEOPHILIC SUBSTITUTION [5,6a,7a]

The two nucleophilic substitution processes we discussed in Sec. 2-4 are referred to as S_N2 and S_N1, respectively, where S_N refers to *n*ucleophilic *s*ubstitution.

S_N2 Bimolecular Nucleophilic Substitution

This is a one-stage process

$$A \colon + B \colon D \to A \colon B + D \colon$$

The 2 in S_N2 stands for *bi*molecular because two entities $A \colon$ and $B \colon D$ undergo bonding changes in the rate-determining step (in this case the only step) of the reaction.

S_N1 Unimolecular Nucleophilic Substitution

The second mechanism was a two-stage process involving a carbonium ion intermediate.

$$B\!\left(\colon D \xrightarrow{\text{slow}} B^{\oplus} + D\colon\right.$$
$$\text{fast} \downarrow A\colon$$
$$B \colon A$$

The reaction is spoken of as *uni*molecular because in the slow and, therefore, rate-determining step only one molecule, B:D, has its bonding changed.

We are now ready to ask more detailed questions about the mechanism of S_N2 and S_N1 reactions. In S_N2 reactions does the nucleophilic reagent $A\colon$ attack from the same side as the leaving group, from the opposite side, or does it attack indiscriminately from all directions? If we choose an optically active alkyl halide, nucleophilic substitution reactions may supply answers.

S_N2 **Mechanism**

When (+)-2-octyl bromide

$$CH_3$$
$$C_6H_{13}—CBr$$
$$H$$

is treated with $I^\ominus$ optically active 2-octyl iodide is obtained but this tells us nothing about direction of attack. From the optical rotation of the iodide we cannot tell whether the arrangement of the groups around the central carbon has been inverted or retained or whether an unequal mixture of inverted and retained product resulted. However, if we treat (+)-2-octyl iodide with $I^\ominus$, racemization results, indicating that at least some attack by $I^\ominus$ occurs from the side that leads to inversion of configuration.

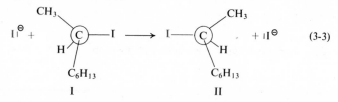

$$(3\text{-}3)$$

I   II

The two forms of 2-octyl iodide **I** and **II** are not identical; in fact, they are mirror images. A 50/50 mixture of **I** and **II** would be a racemic mixture.

If we now use radioactive iodide ion, we can measure the rate of substitution independently by measuring the rate at which radioactivity is incorporated into the organic material. Organic material can be separated from ionized iodide ion simply by pouring samples of reaction mixture into a water–carbon tetrachloride mixture. $I^\ominus$ and $I^{*\ominus}$ dissolve in the former, the octyl iodide in the latter.

$$\overset{*}{I}{}^\ominus + C_6H_{13}\underset{\underset{I}{|}}{C}HCH_3 \longrightarrow C_6H_{13}\underset{\underset{I^*}{|}}{C}HCH_3 + I^\ominus \qquad (3\text{-}4)$$

Rate measurements were as follows:

Second-order rate constant by radioactivity = 13.6 (±1.1) $\times 10^{-4}$

Second-order rate constant by optical activity = 13.1 (±0.1) $\times 10^{-4}$

We conclude from the agreement of the two rates that every time an $I^{\ominus}$ ion attacks the alkyl iodide, it attacks from the back leading to an inversion of configuration. At the transition state, the attacking and leaving iodine atoms are situated approximately on a straight line on opposite sides of the central carbon.

The three groups CH_3, H, and C_6H_{13} are believed to align themselves in a planar position at right angles to the I---C---I line.

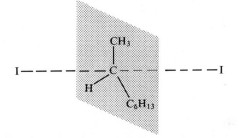

Numerous studies have now been carried out to confirm the generalization that in reactions following the S_N2 pattern, attack is always from the back and the product has a configuration opposite to that of the reagent.

S_N1 Mechanism

We have seen that a number of reactions are best described as involving an alkyl cation intermediate

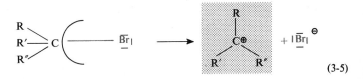

(3-5)

in which the central carbon is surrounded by three bonding electron pairs and no unshared pairs. Now three electron pairs would interfere least with each other when they are at 120° from each other in a plane.

A planar intermediate should be attacked by the nucleophilic reagent A: equally easily from either side so that a racemic mixture RR′R″C–A is predicted in S_N1 reactions.

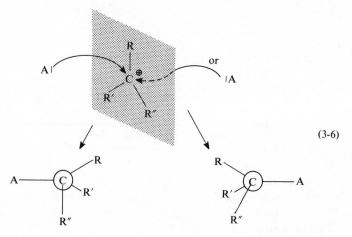

(3-6)

The solvolysis (reaction with solvent molecules) of 1-phenylethyl chloride in ethanol–water mixtures gives close to 90% racemization

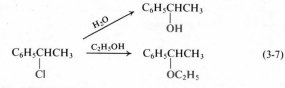

1-Phenylethyl chloride

but most S_N1 reactions produce appreciable amounts of inverted product in addition to racemization. 2-Octyl bromide, which with $C_2H_5O^\ominus$ in ethanol gives 100% inversion typical of S_N2 attack, gave 62% racemization in an S_N1 reaction in a 60% ethanol–40% water solvent. The preponderance of inverted product is generally

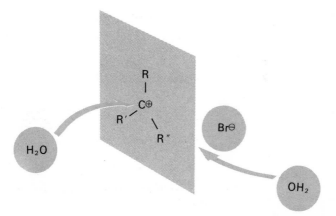

Fig. 3-6. Immediately after the octyl bromide is ionized, the $Br^\ominus$ *formed is still close enough to the carbonium ion to shield it from attack from one side. Thus attack from the opposite side predominates.*

explained by the proposal that the leaving group is still in the vicinity of the carbon atom it has left, thus blocking in part the attack by solvent molecules from that side (Fig. 3-6). Some chemists speak of an ion-pair intermediate in such reactions.

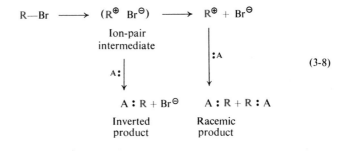

$$R\text{—}Br \longrightarrow (R^\oplus \ Br^\ominus) \longrightarrow R^\oplus + Br^\ominus$$

Ion-pair
intermediate

$$A:R + Br^\ominus \qquad A:R + R:A$$

Inverted   Racemic
product   product

(3-8)

3-4 SOME STEREOCHEMICAL CONSEQUENCES OF THE S_N1 AND S_N2 REACTIONS [2,6b,7a]

A. Cage Structures

Apocamphyl chloride is a cage compound

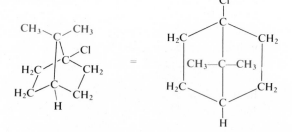

Two representations of apocamphyl chloride

When heated for 21 hours with 30% KOH in an alcohol–water solvent, no reaction occurred. The unreactivity emphasizes what we concluded earlier. For attack by a nucleophilic reagent to occur, the reagent (OH⊖ in this case) must attack on the side of the carbon opposite the group being replaced. If that side is blocked, nothing happens (Fig. 3-7). Perhaps an S_N1 reaction would be more successful.

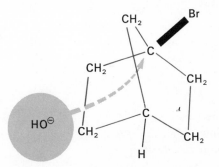

Fig. 3-7. An approaching OH⊖ *has its access to the reaction site blocked by the complex cage structure behind the* C—Br *bond.*

A powerful S_N1 reagent is silver nitrate in water or alcohol, where the $Ag^\oplus$ ion helps to pull off the chloride. When apocamphyl chloride was treated with $AgNO_3$ in alcohol for 48 hours at 79°C, again no reaction occurred. No AgCl was precipitated whereas open (noncage) tertiary halides $R_1R_2R_3CCl$, such as $(CH_3CH_2)_3CCl$, give an AgCl precipitate almost immediately. Now in S_N1 reactions we are not sure that the back of the carbon atom needs to be exposed, even for a solvent molecule. The S_N1 requirement is that the intermediate carbonium ion has a flat planar distribution of groups around the central carbon. In apocamphyl chloride the groups are "pinned back" by the remaining cage structure and are incapable of a planar distribution without serious distortion of bonds from their normal angles. Introducing an extra link in the cage brings the distribution of bonds closer to planar. Whereas I (below) had to be treated with aqueous silver nitrate at 150°C for two days to yield the corresponding alcohol and AgBr, II reacted at room temperature in four hours. An open structure, III, reacts almost instantaneously.

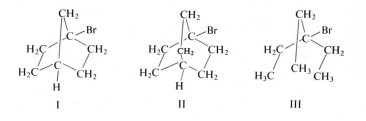

I   II   III

B. Neopentyl Halides

F. C. Whitmore (Pennsylvania State University) in the 1930s and 1940s had pointed to a peculiar unreactivity of an open primary alkyl halide, neopentyl chloride

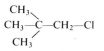

This chloride showed little or no reactivity toward typical nucleo-philic reagents such as $OH^\ominus$, $OC_2H_5^\ominus$, $CN^\ominus$. Quantitative studies in a series of related alkyl bromides showed a very sudden drop in rate when the last methyl group was inserted.

Since all are primary alkyl halides, no back-side blocking of the S_N2 substitution process might be expected. But the construction of models shows that in fact the CH_3 groups of neopentyl bromide do interfere with the incoming or outgoing group in the transition state. If only two CH_3 groups are present as in isobutyl bromide,

Table 3-1 Relative Rates of Reaction of $OC_2H_5^\ominus$ with Primary Alkyl Bromides in Ethyl Alcohol at 55°

Compound	*Relative rate constant*
Methyl CH_3—Br	34.4
Ethyl H H—C—CH_2—Br H	1.95
n-Propyl H CH_3—C—CH_2—Br H	0.547
Isobutyl CH_3 CH_3—C—CH_2—Br H	0.058
Neopentyl CH_3 CH_3—C—CH_2—Br CH_3	0.00000826

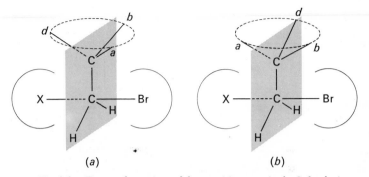

Fig. 3-8. *Two conformations of the transition state in the S_N2 substitution of neopentyl bromide, $(CH_3)_3CCH_2Br$. (Adapted from C. K. Ingold, "Structure and Mechanism in Organic Chemistry," p. 405, Cornell University Press, Ithaca, N.Y., 1953.) Methyl groups are situated at a, b, and d. In conformation A, the CH_3 group at d would strongly interfere with X, while CH_3 groups at a and b would have ample room. In conformation B, steric interference would occur between Br and the CH_3 group at b.*

they can occupy positions *a* and *b* of Fig. 3-8*a* leaving the hydrogen atom at *d*. Steric conflict with the bromine atom or the incoming group X is thus avoided. With three CH_3 groups (at *a, b,* and *d*) steric interference is inevitable no matter how the $C(CH_3)_3$ group is rotated around the vertical C—C bond.

If we switch to the S_N1 mechanism, we find a very different picture. The alkyl cation intermediate involves no steric interference and it should be formed as easily as other $\overset{\oplus}{R}$—CH_2 structures. This in fact is found in practice.

Neopentyl cation

In formic acid as solvent, alkyl bromides react with water by the S_N1 mechanism and with relative rates ethyl 1, *n*-propyl 0.69, neopentyl 0.57. Since the neopentyl cation's reaction with water at the positive carbon would reimpose a rather crowded structure, and for an additional reason to be discussed in Sec. 5-7, rearrangements occur before attack at the primary carbonium ion center is completed.

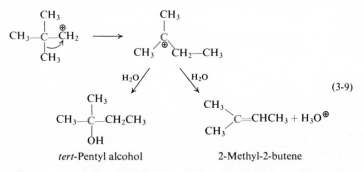

(3-9)

tert-Pentyl alcohol   2-Methyl-2-butene

The alkene (containing the double bond) is formed by an *elimination* mechanism which often accompanies substitution, being particularly prevalent when formation of the alcohol would produce crowding.

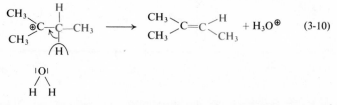

(3-10)

In an alkene, the bonds around the unsaturated carbon are separated by 120° bond angles whereas in an alcohol the bonds are at the tetrahedral angle of 109.5°. One might expect larger amounts of alkene the greater the crowding of alkyl groups.

H. C. Brown (Purdue) has found that whereas *tert*-butyl chloride in 80% aqueous ethanol at 25°C yields 16% alkene, adding three more methyl groups, increases alkene yield to 61%.

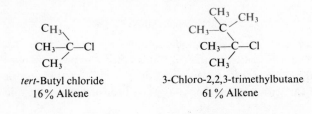

tert-Butyl chloride   3-Chloro-2,2,3-trimethylbutane
16% Alkene   61% Alkene

Crowding in the alkyl halide should also speed up the formation of the planar and more open carbonium ion. When three *tert*-butyl groups crowd around a central carbon, chloride is removed 600 times as fast as when three methyl groups are present:

1   600

Relative rates of solvolysis in 80% aqueous ethanol

We will return to discuss the effect of alkyl groups on alkyl halide reactions when we have examined ways of obtaining energy data for chemical reactions (Secs. 4-3 and 5-2).

3-5 THE ADDITION OF BROMINE TO CARBON—CARBON DOUBLE BONDS [3,6c,7b,10]

When Br_2 adds to ethylene, the product is 1,2-dibromoethane and one is tempted to conclude that the Br_2 molecule straddles the double bond and adds in one simple step.

$$\overset{H}{\underset{H}{>}}C=C\overset{H}{\underset{H}{<}} \xrightarrow{\text{Br—Br}} BrCH_2—CH_2Br \qquad (3\text{-}11)$$

In the presence of sunlight, atoms of bromine are almost certainly involved ($Br_2 \xrightarrow{\text{light}} 2\,Br\cdot$) and such "radical reactions" we will discuss later. In the dark and in solvents in which ions are easily formed, such as water, alcohols, or acetic acid, the mechanism is still not believed to be a simple one, being at least a two-stage process. In the presence of NaCl, NaI, or $NaNO_3$, the anions of these salts become attached to carbon in some of the product

$$Br_2 + CH_2=CH_2 \begin{array}{l} \xrightarrow{\text{NaCl}} BrCH_2—CH_2Cl \\ \xrightarrow{\text{NaI}} BrCH_2—CH_2I \\ \xrightarrow{\text{NaNO}_3} \\ \qquad\quad BrCH_2—CH_2ONO_2 \end{array} \qquad (3\text{-}12)$$

while adding NaBr increases the yield of $BrCH_2CH_2Br$. Thus $Br^\ominus$ from NaBr can compete with the other anions, and a plausible mechanism becomes the cleavage of $Br(-Br$, allowing the first Br (a positive fragment) to become attached to carbon, while $Br^\ominus$ can compete with other anions to form the final product.

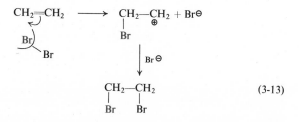

$$(3\text{-}13)$$

But a further complication was discovered. Two ethylene dicarboxylic acids are known, maleic acid, the *cis* acid, with both acid groups on the same side of the double bond, and fumaric acid the *trans* form. Maleic acid with Br_2 yields two optically active mirror image forms, while fumaric acid forms a single symmetrical dibromide.

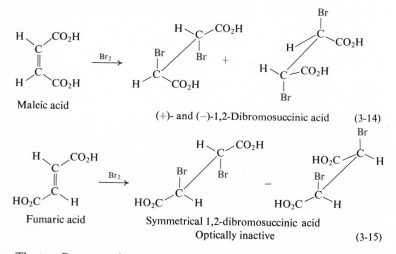

The two Br atoms always seem to add *trans* to each other, on opposite sides of the double bond. If the first Br merely adds to one carbon, forming a planar cation center at the other, then all three products should be formed from either starting material since rotation is possible around a C—C single bond.

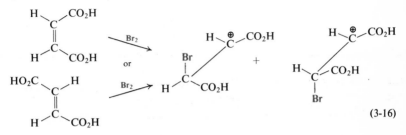

(3-16)

I. Roberts and G. E. Kimball (1906–1967, Columbia University and and A. D. Little Co.) in 1937 suggested that the proposed carbonium ion is not a very plausible intermediate considering the presence of an unshared electron pair on bromine near an electron-deficient positive carbon atom. They proposed a cyclic bromonium ion intermediate.

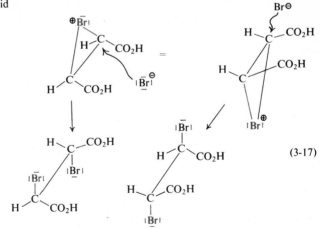

(3-17)

(+)- and (−)-Dibromosuccinic acid

The $Br^{\ominus}$ then displaces $Br^{\oplus}$ by an S_N2 reaction. Similarly for fumaric acid

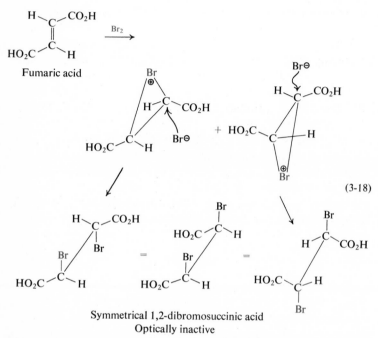

Symmetrical 1,2-dibromosuccinic acid
Optically inactive

(3-18)

Thus the specific *trans* addition of Br_2 to maleic and fumaric acids is accounted for.

SUGGESTED READINGS

1. Allinger, N. L., and J. Allinger: "Structures of Organic Compounds," Prentice-Hall, Inc., Englewood Cliffs, N.J., 1965.
2. Brown, H. C.: The F-, B-, I-Strains, *Rec. Chem. Progr.*, **14**:83(1953).
3. De la Mare, P. B. D.: Kinetics of Thermal Addition of Halogens to Olefinic Compounds, *Quart. Rev.*, **3**:126(1949).
4. Eliel, E. L.: "Stereochemistry of Carbon Compounds," McGraw-Hill Book Company, New York, 1962.

5. Hammett, L. P.: "Physical Organic Chemistry," chap. 6, McGraw-Hill Book Company, New York, 1940.
6. Hine, J.: "Physical Organic Chemistry," 2d ed., (*a*) chaps. 6, 7; (*b*) chap. 7; (*c*) chap. 9, McGraw-Hill Book Company, New York, 1962.
7. Ingold, C. K.: "Structure and Mechanism in Organic Chemistry," (*a*) chap. 7; (*b*) chap. 12, Cornell University Press, Ithaca, N.Y., 1953.
8. Mislow, K.: "Introduction to Stereochemistry," W. A. Benjamin Co., New York, 1965.
9. Morrison, R. J., and R. N. Boyd: "Organic Chemistry," 2d ed., chap. 3, Allyn & Bacon, Inc., Boston, 1966.
10. Roberts, I., and G. E. Kimball: The Halogenation of Ethylenes, *J. Am. Chem. Soc.*, **59**:947(1937).
11. Senior, J.: An Evaluation of the Structural Theory of Organic Chemistry, *J. Chem. Educ.*, **12**:409, 465 (1935).

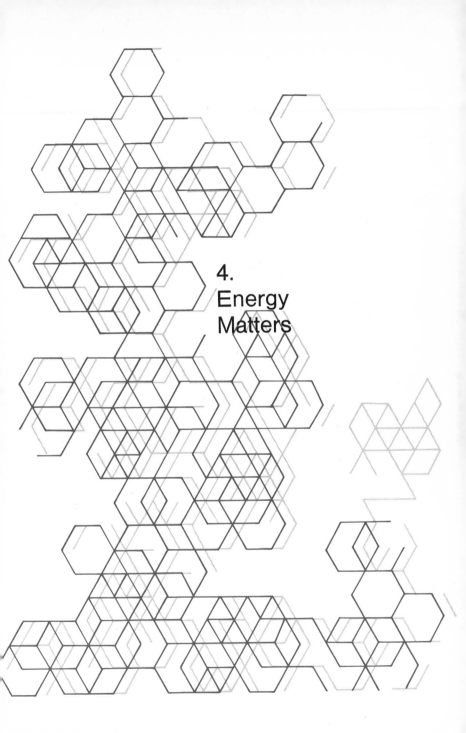

4.
Energy
Matters

4-1 ENERGY DISTRIBUTION AMONG MOLECULES
[1*a*,2*a*,5*b*]

It takes energy to climb a mountain. It takes energy to dig a tunnel but none to roll down one if its slope happens to be downward. It takes energy to separate two things that are connected or have an attraction for each other, like iron and a magnet. It takes energy to break a bond. At the absolute zero of temperature, $0°K$, no bonds can be broken. At high enough temperatures no bonds can be formed. Only in the intermediate region is change possible. We happen to live in that region; only in that region is thought and human activity of any kind possible—including the study of chemical reactions.

The faster a molecule moves, the higher its kinetic energy. If its velocity is v and its mass m, the kinetic energy is $\frac{1}{2}mv^2$. The higher the average kinetic energy of a group of molecules, the higher the temperature. The absolute temperature is a measure of the average kinetic energy.

$$\frac{T_1}{T_2} = \frac{(KE)_1}{(KE)_2} \tag{4-1}$$

The molecular energies are not likely all to be the same or to be uniformly distributed over all possible values. The lowest possible energy is zero, but at the upper end, a collection of molecules at any finite temperature is not likely to have any absolutely maximum energy. Few molecules will have extremely high velocities or energies, and the higher the energy the fewer the number of molecules. If we graphed number of molecules against energy, the graph would look something like this

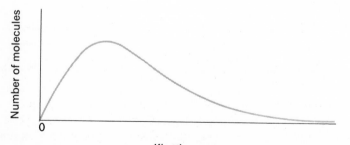

Fig. 4-1. Distribution of molecular energies.

and at a higher temperature, with the same number of molecules, the area under the curve would remain the same but more molecules would have higher energies, so that the top of the curve, the maximum, would shift to the right and be lower. Suppose two molecules A and B

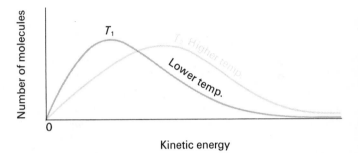

Fig. 4-2.   Distribution of molecular energies at two temperatures.

collide. We can graph the total kinetic energy of colliding molecules against the number of collisions with that total energy. The graph will look about the same as the earlier one. Now, if bonds need to

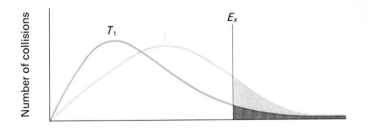

Total energy of colliding molecules

Fig. 4-3.   Distribution of collision energies.

be broken in molecule A or B, the total collision energy must at least equal the energy of the bond to be broken. Otherwise the two molecules will separate again after collision. Suppose the minimum energy for reaction needed by collisions is E_x, then, only that fraction of all the collisions shown by the shaded area in Fig. 4-3, can lead to reaction, that is, to product formation. Note that at a higher temperature T_2 a very much larger fraction of all collisions has the requisite energy. As a rule of thumb chemists often say that an increase of temperature of 10°C will double or triple the rate of reaction. This is explained by the fact that even though the average energy at 25°C (298°K) only goes up by $\frac{10}{298} \times 100\%$ (i.e., about 3%) for a 10°C rise, the number of collisions with energy above the critical energy for reaction E_x may well double. Thus a study of the effect of temperature on reaction rate should give us an insight into the magnitude of E_x (see Sec. 4-2). It also emphasizes the importance of knowing the exact temperature at which a reaction is run, and of running two reactions whose rates are to be compared at precisely the same temperature. If a 10° change in temperature will double the rate, a 1° fluctuation will mean an uncertainty of approximately 10% in the rate measurement. For most organic reactions studied to elucidate mechanisms, the temperature accordingly is controlled at least within 0.02°C.

The rates of the displacement reaction of N,N-dimethylaniline with methyl iodide

$$C_6H_5-N\begin{array}{c}CH_3\\ \\CH_3\end{array} + CH_3-I \longrightarrow C_6H_5-\overset{\overset{\displaystyle CH_3}{|\oplus}}{\underset{\underset{\displaystyle CH_3}{|}}{N}}-CH_3 \quad I^\ominus \qquad (4\text{-}2)$$

were measured in nitrobenzene at various temperatures.

Table 4-1 Rate Constants of the Dimethylaniline–Methyl Iodide Reaction at Various Temperatures

$T°C$	k liters/mole sec
24.8	8.39 $\times 10^{-5}$
40.1	21.0 $\times 10^{-5}$
60.0	77.2 $\times 10^{-5}$
80.1	238 $\times 10^{-5}$

If the rate constants are plotted against temperature we obtain a curve as in Fig. 4-4.

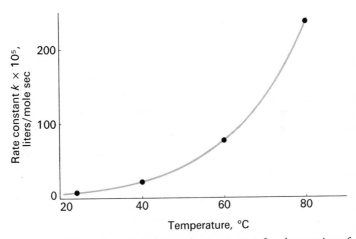

Fig. 4-4. *Temperature dependence of rate constant for the reaction of N,N-dimethylaniline and methyl iodide in nitrobenzene.*

4-2 ACTIVATION ENERGY E_a [1a,2a,5a]

Svante Arrhenius (Norwegian, 1859–1927) found that on plotting the logarithm of the rate constant against the reciprocal of the absolute temperature T an approximate straight line was obtained.

This linear relation (Fig. 4-5) can be expressed as the equation

$$\log k = -\frac{A}{T} + B \qquad (4\text{-}3)$$

where A and B are constants, or, for two temperatures, T_1 and T_2

$$\log \frac{k_2}{k_1} = \log k_2 - \log k_1 = A\left[\frac{1}{T_1} - \frac{1}{T_2}\right] \qquad (4\text{-}4)$$

The relationship has also been expressed in natural logarithms ($\ln k = 2.303 \log k$) as

$$\ln k = -\frac{E_a}{RT} + \ln D \qquad (4\text{-}5)$$

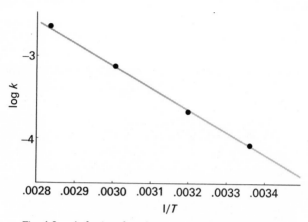

Fig. 4-5. Arrhenius plot of rate constant–temperature data.

or

$$\ln \frac{k_2}{k_1} = \frac{E_a}{R}\left[\frac{1}{T_1} - \frac{1}{T_2}\right]$$ (4-6)

where **R** is the gas constant, 1.987 cal/deg mole, D is another constant and E_a is known as the Arrhenius *activation energy*. An alternative form of this expression is

$$k = D\,e^{-E_a/RT}$$ (4-7)

where $e^{-E_a/RT}$ is recognized by chemists as an expression derived by L. Boltzmann in the nineteenth century for the fraction of collisions that have a minimum energy E_a. It was then assumed that D must be a measure of the number of collisions per second and this collision frequency could be calculated if some reasonable assumptions were made about sizes, velocities, and concentrations. The activation energy can be obtained by substituting values of k_1, k_2, T_1, and T_2 in Eq. (4-6), or from graphs such as Fig. 4-5 whose slope is $-E_a/2.303R$ [cf. Eq. (4-5)].

Problem 4-1

Compute the activation energy for the temperature range 24.8°C to 60.0°C from the data in Table 4-1. Check your value by a graphical determination of the slope of a log k vs. $1/T$ plot.

Answer. Substituting in Eq. (4-6)

$$\ln\frac{k_2}{k_1} = 2.303\left(\log\frac{k_2}{k_1}\right) = 2.303(\log k_2 - \log k_1)$$

$$= \frac{E_a}{\mathbf{R}}\left[\frac{1}{T_1} - \frac{1}{T_2}\right]$$

we obtain

$$2.303(\log 77.2 \times 10^{-5} - \log 8.39 \times 10^{-5}) = \frac{E_a}{1.987}\left[\frac{1}{298.0} - \frac{1}{333.2}\right]$$

Hence

$$E_a = \frac{2.303 \times 1.0638 \times 1.987}{0.000355}$$

$$= 12,400 \text{ cal}$$

From Fig. 4-5, the slope is $-2,780$. Setting this equal to $-E_a/2.303\mathbf{R}$, we obtain

$$E_a = 2.303\mathbf{R} \times 2,780$$

$$= 2.303 \times 1.987 \times 2,780$$

$$= 12,700 \text{ cal}$$

4-3 THE NEED FOR PROPER ORIENTATION [1a,2a,4,5a]

By substituting the experimentally obtained value of E_a in Eq. (4-7) we often obtain a value for D much smaller than that calculated from collision calculations. The clear implication is that only a fraction of collisions leads to reaction even when the requisite minimum energy is present. The reason is not hard to find. When methyl bromide reacts with hydroxide ion we have already discovered that the reagent must attack the carbon from the direction opposite to the C—Br bond. All attacks from other directions, no matter how energetic, presumably cause no chemical change. The constant D of Eq. (4-7) is, therefore, resolved into two constants PZ of which Z is the collision number (the number of collisions occurring between reactant molecules in unit volume per unit time) and P is a probability or steric factor giving the fraction of energetically favorable collisions that are also sterically favorable— collisions that occur with favorable orientations for reaction to take place. Clearly if the H of the $OH^\ominus$ approaches an H of CH_3Br we are not likely to find the C—Br bond breaking or an O—C bond formed. Hence $k = PZe^{-E_a/RT}$.

Thus a study of the temperature dependence of reaction rates gives us information both about the energy requisite for reaction to take place and about steric (or spatial) requirements.

Sometimes the graph of rate versus temperature is very different from the pattern discussed so far (Figs. 4-4 and 4-6a). An explosive

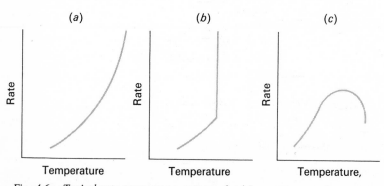

Fig. 4-6. *Typical rate–temperature patterns for* (a) *common organic reactions,* (b) *explosive reactions,* (c) *enzyme-catalyzed reactions.*

reaction follows Fig. 4-6b while an enzyme-catalyzed reaction can usually be represented by Fig. 4-6c. The last graph shows a maximum or optimum rate at one temperature. Higher temperatures slow down the reaction by modifying (deactivating) the enzyme, reducing its

Table 4-2 Second-order Rate Constants, k_2, Energies of Activation, E_a, and PZ Values in Reaction $RBr + C_2H_5O^{\ominus}$ in ethanol at 55°C for a series of primary alkyl bromides[a]

	Methyl CH_3Br	*Ethyl* C_2H_5Br	*n-Propyl* $CH_3CH_2CH_2Br$	*Isobutyl* $(CH_3)_2CHCH_2Br$	*Neopentyl* $(CH_3)_3CCH_2Br$
$k_2 \times 10^3$ liters/mole sec	34.4	1.95	0.547	0.058	0.00000826
E_a kcal/mole	20.0	21.0	$\cdots$	22.8	26.2
$PZ \times 10^{-11}$ liters/mole sec	7.2	2.1	$\cdots$	0.95	0.023

[a] From I. Dostrovsky and E. D. Hughes, *J. Chem. Soc.*, 159, 1946.

ability to act as a suitable surface on which reacting molecules can undergo efficient chemical change.

Table 4-2 shows rates, activation energies, and *PZ* values for the sequence of alkyl halides, methyl to neopentyl bromide, reacting with $C_2H_5O^\ominus$ in ethanol, a reaction which we have already discussed

$$C_2H_5\bar{\underline{O}}{}^{\ominus}\ |\ +\ R{-}\bar{\underline{B}}r\ | \rightarrow C_2H_5\bar{\underline{O}}{-}R\ +\ |\bar{\underline{B}}r\ |^{\ominus} \tag{4-8}$$

in Sec. 3-4. In this case the reduction in rate from left to right is accompanied both by an increase in the activation energy and a decrease in the probability factor. The changes are particularly striking in moving from isobutyl to neopentyl bromide where the 7,000-fold decrease in rate is due to a major increase in activation energy (3.4 kcal/mole) and a 40-fold decrease in the probability factor. The latter alone reduces the rate by a factor of 40. The change in activation energy lowers the rate by another factor of about 175 ($40 \times 175 = 7,000$).

Problem 4-2

Determine the effect of changes in activation energy on rate by calculating the factor $e^{-E_a/RT}$ (the fraction of collisions having energy above E_a) for a reaction at 27°C, if the activation energy is (*a*) 6 kcal/mole, (*b*) 12 kcal/mole, (*c*) 18 kcal/mole ($R = 1.986 \simeq 2.00$ cal/deg mole).

Answer

$T = 273 + 27 = 300°K$
$RT = 2.00 \times 300 = 600$ cal/mole
(*a*) $E_a = 6$ kcal/mole $= 6,000$ cal/mole
$e^{-E_a/RT} = e^{-6000/600} = e^{-10} = 4.54 \times 10^{-5}$

Thus about five collisions in 100,000 at 27°C have energy above 6 kcal/mole. (Values of e^x and e^{-x} for values of x from 0 to 10 can be found in mathematical tables such as the Handbook of Chemistry and Physics.)

(b) $E_a = 12$ kcal/mole $= 12,000$ cal/mole

$e^{-E_a/RT} = e^{-12000/600} = e^{-20} = (4.54 \times 10^{-5})^2 = 2.06 \times 10^{-9}$

Thus two collisions in a billion have the requisite energy.

(c) $E_a = 18$ kcal/mole $= 18,000$ cal/mole

$e^{-E_a/RT} = e^{-18000/600} = e^{-30} = (4.54 \times 10^{-5})^3 = 9.36 \times 10^{-14}$

Here nine collisions in 100 million billion have the requisite energy.

Thus at 27°C a change of activation energy from 6 to 12 kcal (*PZ* remaining constant) would lead to a reduction in rate from 4.54×10^{-5} to 2.06×10^{-9} or a factor of 20,000. A change of E_a from 12 to 18 kcal would lead to a further reduction in rate by the same factor.

There are no energy and *PZ* data in Table 4-2 for the ethyl to *n*-propyl change. However, a number of ethyl and *n*-propyl halide substitution reactions have been studied at different temperatures with the interesting result that *n*-propyl halides usually react more slowly than the corresponding ethyl halides, even though the activation energy is the same or nearly the same for both. The reduction in rate is, therefore, largely or totally due to a lowered *PZ* term, to a reduction in the chance of attaining a favorable orientation for reaction.

Table 4-3 Comparison of Ethyl Halide and *n*-Propyl Halide Reactions

	E_a kcal	Rate $(n - Pr)$/Rate (Et)
$C_2H_5Br + LiBr^a$ in acetone	17.5 ⎫	
$CH_3CH_2CH_2Br + LiBr^a$ in acetone	17.5 ⎭	0.66
$C_2H_5I + LiBr^a$ in acetone	19.0 ⎫	
$CH_3CH_2CH_2I + LiBr^a$ in acetone	19.0 ⎭	0.69

^{a} = radioactive bromine.

How can E_a and *PZ* be related to energy quantities more commonly obtained for reactions? The enthalpy of reaction ΔH for

$$a\text{A} + b\text{B} \rightarrow c\text{C} + d\text{D} \qquad (4\text{-}9)$$

is the heat absorbed in the formation of *c* moles of C and *d* moles of D from *a* moles of A and *b* moles of B. If the reaction is exothermic, ΔH is negative and the products lie at a lower enthalpy level than the reactants (see Fig. 4-7).

ΔH values are usually given, and in this book are always given, for reactants starting at 25°C and products ending at 25°C. Formulas refer to substances in their most stable state at this temperature. Thus CH_4 means gaseous methane, C_2H_5OH liquid ethanol (see Fig. 4-8).

If the reaction is slow due to a significant energy of activation, we can show an energy barrier on our diagram. The extra enthalpy needed to cross the barrier is given the symbol $\Delta H^{\ddagger}$ and called the enthalpy of activation. For the reverse reaction there will be a larger enthalpy of activation $\Delta_{rev}^{\ddagger}$, since for an exothermic reaction it has to be equal to the ΔH of reaction plus the $\Delta H^{\ddagger}$ for the forward reaction. See Fig. 4-9. The difference between the two enthalpies of activation must equal the enthalpy of reaction. Examples are given

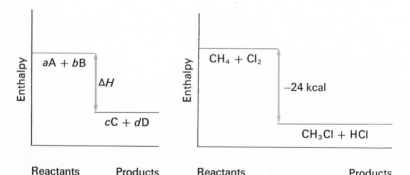

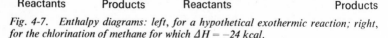

Fig. 4-7. Enthalpy diagrams: left, for a hypothetical exothermic reaction; right, for the chlorination of methane for which $\Delta H = -24$ kcal.

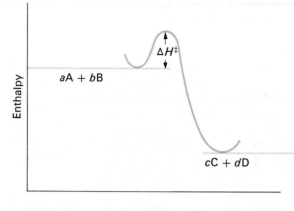

Reactants   Barrier   Products

Fig. 4-8. Enthalpy diagram showing energy barrier.

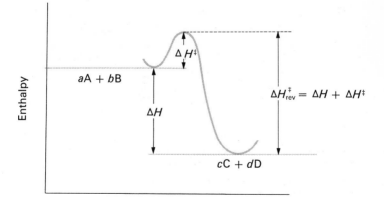

Reaction path

Fig. 4-9. Enthalpies of activation and reaction.

in Fig. 4-10 for the removal of hydrogen atoms from methane by halogen atoms showing an exothermic reaction when chlorine attacks, while bromine attack is endothermic.

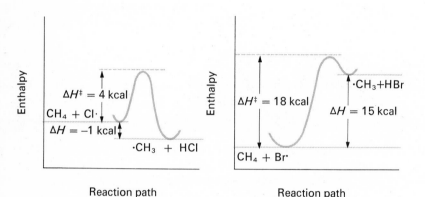

Fig. 4-10. Enthalpy changes for hydrogen abstraction from methane, $CH_4 + X\cdot \rightarrow CH_3\cdot + HX$, (a) by chlorine atoms, (b) by bromine atoms.

The energy barrier and thus the need for an activation energy can perhaps be more easily understood in terms of Fig. 4-11 depicting a pass across a mountain range from one valley to another. The maxima in Figs. 4-8 to 4-10 are thus seen to be the lowest energies needed to cross the range. With considerable excess energy, a pair of colliding molecules may cross the range at a different point, corresponding to a modified transition-state configuration. A wide pass through the mountain range (Fig. 4-11a) would suggest a high probability of traversing it, while a narrow pass (Fig. 4-11b) corresponds to a much smaller probability term.

4-4 ABSOLUTE REACTION RATE THEORY [1b,3a,5a]

Is ΔH^+ the same as E_a, the activation energy we discussed earlier as something obtainable experimentally? The answer is—almost. The theory of absolute reaction rates developed by Henry Eyring (University of Utah) and others assumes an equilibrium between

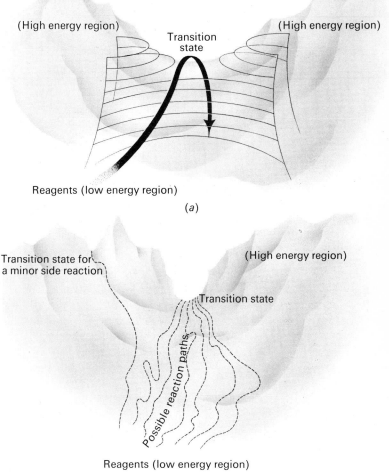

(High energy region)   Transition state   (High energy region)

Reagents (low energy region)

(*a*)

Transition state for a minor side reaction   (High energy region)

Transition state

Possible reaction paths

Reagents (low energy region)

(*b*)

Fig. 4-11. Mountain range analogy for energy profile. The transition state corresponds to the lowest available pass. (a) A wide pass suggests a high probability of traversing the range, (b) a narrow pass corresponds to a low PZ term. (After J. E. Leffler and E. Grunwald, "Rates and Equilibria of Organic Reactions," pp. 65–68, John Wiley & Sons, Inc., New York, 1963.)

reactants and entities in the transition state (X^+)—the arrangement of atoms at the top of the energy barrier. If we assume a real equilibrium we can define an equilibrium constant K^+ for the reaction

$$a\text{A} + b\text{B} \ \rightleftharpoons \ \text{X}^+ \tag{4-10}$$

where

$$K^+ = \frac{[\text{X}^+]}{[\text{A}]^a[\text{B}]^b} \tag{4-11}$$

and the equilibrium constant is related to the free energy of activation ΔG^+ by the relations

$$\Delta G^+ = -2.303\,\mathbf{R}T\log K^+ \quad \text{or} \quad K^+ = e^{-\Delta G^+/\mathbf{R}T} \tag{4-12}$$

but

$$\Delta\text{G}^+ = \Delta H^+ - T\Delta S^+ \tag{4-13}$$

the usual thermodynamic relation between free energy change, enthalpy change ΔH^+, and entropy change ΔS^+. ΔS^+ measures the change in entropy between reactants and transition state, that is, the difference between the order, or organization, or freedom of movement of reactants and transition state. If the atoms are more ordered, or more restricted in their freedom to move, as reactants change to transition state, then ΔS^+ will be negative. Whenever two reactants come together to form a transition-state configuration one expects such an entropy decrease, because the two reactants initially were free to move relative to each other and this freedom is lost as the transition state is formed. The entropy of activation is a very similar measure to the term P in the equation $k = PZe^{-E_a/\mathbf{R}T}$ (log P should be proportional to ΔS^+).

By the theory of absolute reaction rates, for most reactions in solution, the enthalpy of activation ΔH^+ differs from the Arrhenius activation energy E_a by an amount depending on the temperature, $\mathbf{R}T$

$$\Delta H^+ = E_a - \mathbf{R}T \tag{4-14}$$

Since $\mathbf{R} = 2$ cal/deg mole, $\mathbf{R}T$ is about 600 cal (0.6 kcal) at room temperature and thus quite small compared with activation energies usually obtained.

The theory of absolute reaction rates assumes—with some justification from statistical mechanics—that all activated complexes (the configurations in the transition state) form products at the same rate. The universal rate constant for the formation of products from the complex is given by the theory as $\mathbf{k}T/h$ where $\mathbf{k}$ is Boltzmann's constant (1.38×10^{-16} erg/degree), h is Planck's constant (6.62×10^{-27} erg-sec), and $\mathbf{k}T/h$ at room temperature equals 6×10^{12}/sec.

The rate of reaction at a given temperature then depends only on the concentration of activated complex. At room temperature

$$\text{Rate} = 6 \times 10^{12} \times [\text{activated complex}] \tag{4-15}$$

but

$$K^+ = \frac{[\text{activated complex}]}{[A]^a[B]^b} \tag{4-16}$$

and

$$\text{Rate} = k[A]^a[B]^b = 6 \times 10^{12} K^+[A]^a[B]^b \tag{4-17}$$

Therefore, the rate constant

$$k = 6 \times 10^{12} K^+ \tag{4-18}$$

or, in general, at temperature T

$$k = \frac{\mathbf{k}T}{h} K^+ \tag{4-19}$$

substituting for K^+ from Eq. (4-12)

$$k = \frac{\mathbf{k}T}{h} e^{-\Delta G^+/\mathbf{R}T} \tag{4-20}$$

but since

$$\Delta G^+ = \Delta H^+ - T\Delta S^+ \quad [\text{eq. (4-13)}]$$

we obtain

$$k = \frac{\mathbf{k}T}{h} e^{\Delta S^+/\mathbf{R}} e^{-\Delta H^+/\mathbf{R}T} \tag{4-21}$$

This is the general equation relating rate of reaction with enthalpy and entropy terms according to the theory of absolute reaction rates.

For the reaction of ethyl and *n*-propyl bromides with thiophenolate ion, $C_6H_5S^\ominus$, in methanol at 20°C

$$C_6H_5\bar{S}^{\ominus} + RBr \rightarrow C_6H_5\bar{S}{-}R + Br^\ominus \tag{4-22}$$

the following data were obtained

	k_2 liters/mole sec	ΔH^+ kcal/mole	ΔS^+ kcal/deg
CH_3CH_2Br	39.1×10^{-4}	18.1	$- 7.7$
$CH_3CH_2CH_2Br$	25.6×10^{-4}	17.7	-10.0

These data confirm our earlier conclusion that the 30% reduction in rate from ethyl to *n*-propyl bromide is due to a large increase in the negative entropy corresponding to a lower probability factor for attaining the transition state while the energy term remains almost unchanged. In fact, the enthalpy of activation, ΔH^+, goes *down* by 0.4 unit which alone would have led to an increase in rate.

4-5 ENERGY PROFILES [3a,4]

We can now draw energy profiles for the S_N1 and S_N2 reaction or for any reaction whose mechanism has been established.

S_N2

The S_N2 process is complete in one stage, the transition state corresponding to the arrangement where the nucleophilic reagent is partially bound and the leaving group is not completely severed (Fig. 4-12).

S_N1

The S_N1 process, on the other hand, involves an unstable intermediate, the carbonium ion I (Fig. 4-13).

The enthalpy of activation, ΔH^+ indicates the highest level the enthalpy must reach from its reactant stage. If the enthalpy of activation between the intermediate carbonium ion and product, ΔH^+, is high also, it would be possible to isolate the intermediate, and this has been done under certain special conditions as described in Sec. 2-4.

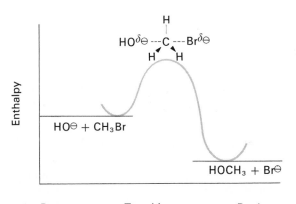

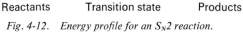

Reactants   Transition state   Products

Fig. 4-12.   Energy profile for an S_N2 reaction.

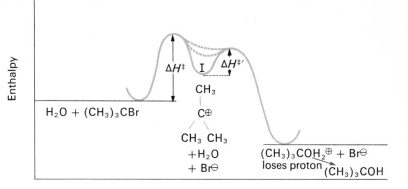

Reactants   Intermediates   Products

Fig. 4-13.   Energy profile for an S_N1 reaction.

If the valley is very small or nonexistent, as indicated by the broken lines, then the S_N1 mechanism merges into the S_N2 mechanism, and no intermediate can be detected.

4-6 CATALYSIS [2b]

A catalyst is a substance which influences the rate of a reaction without itself being consumed in the reaction. At one time the catalyst was conceived of as acting almost by magic, changing the rate without being involved. We now know in many instances the nature of the involvement and are confident that in all cases the catalyst participates in the reaction, its only difference from reagents being that, at a certain stage, catalyst molecules or ions are liberated again, thus permitting them to operate on other reagents also.

Thus iodide ions speed up the rate of hydrolysis of methyl bromide.

$$\text{Slow:} \quad CH_3Br + 2\,H_2O \longrightarrow CH_3OH + Br^\ominus + H_3O^\oplus \qquad (4\text{-}23)$$

$$\text{Faster:} \quad CH_3Br + 2\,H_2O \xrightarrow{\ I^\ominus\ } CH_3OH + Br^\ominus + H_3O^\oplus \qquad (4\text{-}24)$$

A speeding up of a reaction must mean the lowering of the energy barrier, or an increase in the entropy of activation (or PZ term), or both.

One explanation of the iodide catalysis is that methyl iodide is formed and then hydrolyzes

$$I^\ominus + CH_3Br \rightarrow CH_3I + Br^\ominus \qquad (4\text{-}25)$$

$$CH_3I + 2\,H_2O \rightarrow CH_3OH + H_3O^\oplus + I^\ominus \qquad (4\text{-}26)$$

The methyl bromide reaction with iodide ion [Eq. (4-25)] can be studied in the absence of water (in acetone for instance) and is known to proceed quite rapidly. The methyl iodide reaction [Eq. (4-26)] can be studied under the same conditions as Eq. (4-23) and is known to go about twice as fast. Thus our proposed mechanism is not only plausible, it is a mechanism that *must* interfere, the iodide ion helping to hydrolyze much of the methyl bromide by this alternative mechanism. The energy profile of the two processes can be represented as

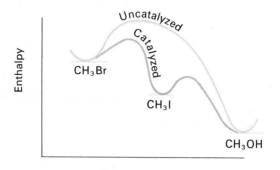

Fig. 4-14. Catalyzed and uncatalyzed paths for the hydrolysis of methyl bromide.

The iodide-catalyzed profile has a lower enthalpy of activation than the uncatalyzed path and is, therefore, preferred when $I^{\ominus}$ is present. Entropy or orientation factors are not likely to play a significant role, although the $I^{\ominus}$ is considerably larger than the water molecule so that the number of collisions will increase.

4-7 ENZYME CATALYSIS AND ENZYME MODELS [3*b*,5*c*,6,7]

Many reactions are catalyzed by surfaces, and numerous industrial processes, such as the production of sulfuric acid where SO_2 is first oxidized with air to SO_3 on a platinized asbestos surface, make use of this fact. Enzymes carry out many organic reactions rapidly at room temperature and at almost neutral pH whereas organic chemists perform the same syntheses slowly at high temperatures and under strongly acidic or basic conditions in the absence of enzyme catalysts. An enzyme, being a complex protein, has a very uneven and chemically nonuniform surface with different groups sticking out at different points. Only a certain region, the active site, performs the catalytic function and then only for one reaction involving often only a single molecule or two specific reacting molecules. Usually an enzyme that catalyzes the reaction of one optically active form is totally inactive toward its enantiomorph, its mirror-image form. Although the details of enzyme action have not been worked out and are currently under active study, enzymes are believed to act by holding the reagents on surfaces ideally suited for them and often reacting with them chemically, as the iodide ion did with methyl bromide, forming an intermediate which then reacts further to form products and to regenerate the enzyme. The effectiveness of enzyme catalysis can be seen from the data in Table 4-4 for the decomposition of urea to carbon dioxide and ammonia

$$CO(NH_2)_2 + H_2O \rightarrow CO_2 + 2\,NH_3 \qquad (4\text{-}27)$$

The effect of the enzyme urease[1] at room temperature on rate constant, *PZ* factor, and energy of activation is startling. Urease increases the rate by a factor of 10^{13} in spite of $40°C$ lower temperature and almost no acidity. This is achieved by a 1,000-fold increase in the probability factor and a cut of the energy of activation to less than a third.

Table 4-4   Rate Data for the Decomposition of Urea[a]

Catalyst	$T°C$	k	PZ	E_a
		liters/mole sec		*kcal/mole*
$H_3O^\oplus$	62.0	7.4×10^{-7}	1.8×10^{10}	24.6
Urease	20.8	5.0×10^6	1.7×10^{13}	6.8

[a] From K. J. Laidler, "Chemical Kinetics," McGraw-Hill Book Company, New York, 482 (1965).

[1] Enzymes in this book are designated by their trivial names. The substance attacked (i.e., the "substrate") is normally listed, and modified by the suffix—*ase*. Thus urease decomposes urea. There are exceptions. Peroxidases involve hydrogen peroxide as oxidizing agents. The enzyme that catalyzes hydrogen peroxide decomposition is called catalase (see below).

Sometimes, as in the decomposition of hydrogen peroxide, a nonenzymatic catalyst can do as well as an enzyme as far as the *PZ* term is concerned.

Table 4-5 Rate Data for the Decomposition of Hydrogen Peroxide[a]

$2 H_2O_2 \rightarrow 2 H_2O + O_2$

Catalyst	$T°C$	k	PZ	E_a
		liters/mole sec		*kcal/mole*
None	22.0	10^{-7}	10^6	17–18
$Fe^{2\oplus}$	22.0	56.0	1.8×10^9	10.1
Catalase	22.0	3.5×10^7	6.4×10^8	1.7

[a] K. J. Laidler, "Chemical Kinetics," McGraw-Hill Book Company, New York, 482 (1965).

In this reaction, ferrous ion is a little more effective than the enzyme catalase in raising the *PZ* term but the catalase reaction is still a million times faster because of an enormously lowered energy of activation.

Swain (MIT) and Brown in 1952 demonstrated a remarkable catalytic effect due to the presence of two functional groups located in a molecule in the proper position to influence a reaction effectively. (+)-Glucose exists in two forms. When crystallized from water below 98°C it has a mp of 146°C and an initial optical rotation in water of +112° which slowly drops to +52.7°. This is α-(+)-glucose. If glucose is crystallized at temperatures above 98°C (by evaporation of boiling water from the solution) β-(+)-glucose forms with mp 150°C and a rotation rising from +19° to +52.7°. This phenomenon of changing rotation is known as *mutarotation* and is catalyzed by both acids and bases. Mutarotation is considerably accelerated when both an acid and a base are present. Yet 2-hydroxypyridine, which contains both an acidic (OH) and a basic ($\geqslant$N:) group, at 0.001M concentration proved to be 7,000 times as effective a catalyst in such a mutarotation as a mixture of $0.001M$ phenol and $0.001M$ pyridine.

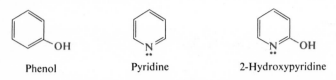

Phenol   Pyridine   2-Hydroxypyridine

Mutarotation involves the opening of a six-membered ring and its closing in two possible directions. In the open-chain form the CHO group is free to rotate and hence can close the ring in two distinct ways.

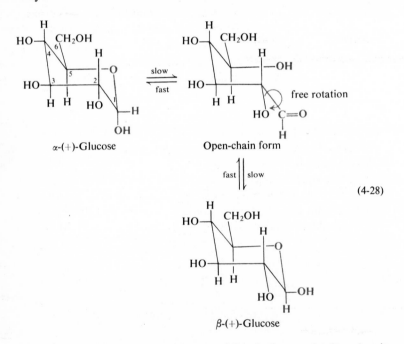

α-(+)-Glucose   Open-chain form

β-(+)-Glucose

(4-28)

The effectiveness of the 2-hydroxypyridine is due to the fact that it can donate a proton with its acid group while accepting a proton with its nitrogen, forming a cyclic intermediate in the process. Separate

acid and base molecules would be likely to interfere with each other
if they were to operate together in a similar manner.

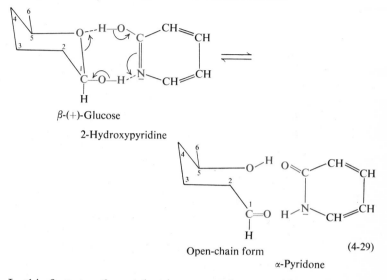

β-(+)-Glucose

2-Hydroxypyridine

Open-chain form   (4-29)

α-Pyridone

In this first step the catalyst is converted to α-pyridone. When the
open chain is converted back to α- or β-(+)-glucose, the 2-hydroxy-
pyridine is re-formed.

Since water can act both as acid and base and, therefore, mildly
catalyzes mutarotation, the above studies were carried out in benzene
solution. But glucose is not soluble in benzene and, therefore, was
methylated (conversion of OH to OCH_3 groups) at all positions not
involved in the catalysis, that is, at positions 2, 3, 4, and 6.

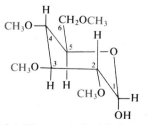

2,3,4,6-Tetramethyl-α-(+)-glucose

The mutarotation of glucose is catalyzed in cells by an enzyme, mutarotase. It is plausible to suggest that its effectiveness is due to a set of concerted reactions similar to that demonstrated for 2-hydroxypyridine.

SUGGESTED READINGS

1. Frost, A. A., and R. G. Pearson: "Kinetics and Mechanisms," 2d ed., (*a*) chap. 4; (*b*) chap. 5, John Wiley & Sons, Inc., New York, 1961.
2. Hammett, L. P.: "Physical Organic Chemistry," (*a*) chap. 4; (*b*) chap. 6, McGraw-Hill Book Company, New York, 1940.
3. Hine, J.: "Physical Organic Chemistry," 2d ed., (*a*) chap. 7; (*b*) chap. 11, McGraw-Hill Book Company, New York, 1962.
4. Ingold, C. K.: "Structure and Mechanism in Organic Chemistry," chap. 7, Cornell University Press, Ithaca, N.Y., 1953.
5. Laidler, K. J.: "Chemical Kinetics," 2d ed., (*a*) chap. 3; (*b*) chaps. 3, 5; (*c*) chap. 9, McGraw-Hill Book Company, New York, 1965.
6. Raw, I.: Enzymes—How They Operate, *Chemistry*, **40**:8 (June 1967).
7. Swain, C. G., and J. F. Brown, Jr.: Polyfunctional Catalysis, *J. Am. Chem. Soc.*, **74**:2538 (1952).

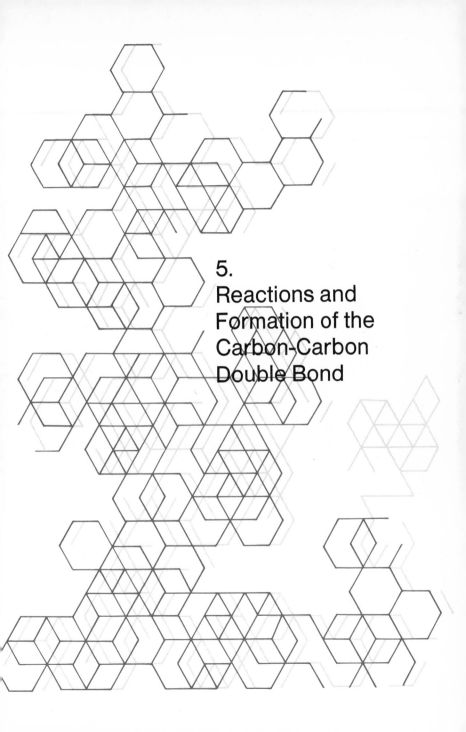

5.
Reactions and Formation of the Carbon-Carbon Double Bond

5-1 INTRODUCTION [1a,3]

A double bond is stronger than a single bond—but not twice as strong. Bond energies for the cleavage of single bonds C—C → C· + ·C and double bonds C=C → C: + :C are

Bond energies, kcal/mole

C—C	83
C=C	~140

It is much easier to break one bond of the double bond (C=C → Ċ—Ċ) than to break a carbon—carbon single bond. Numerous reactions of the type

$$A—B + \;\;\;C=C\;\;\; \rightarrow A—C—C—B$$

are known and we have already discussed in detail the addition of bromine, Br_2, to double bonds, a process which, in the absence of light and in polar solvents, occurs exclusively by trans addition, the two bromine atoms adding on opposite sides of the double bond.

In the tricarboxylic acid cycle, also called the citric acid or Krebs

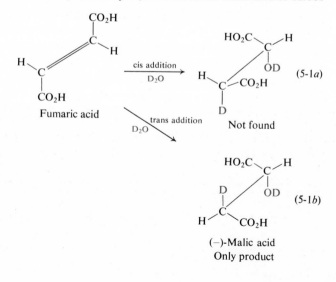

Fumaric acid

cis addition D_2O

trans addition D_2O

Not found (5-1a)

(−)-Malic acid
Only product (5-1b)

cycle (after the original proponent Hans Krebs), the cellular metabolism of fats to carbon dioxide involves as one of its steps the addition of a molecule of water to fumaric acid, catalyzed by the enzyme fumarase. By use of deuterium labeling—the use of heavy water, D_2O—the reaction has been found to proceed solely by trans addition (5-1a and b).

Similarly the enzyme aconitase catalyzes another step in the cycle, the hydration of *cis*-aconitic acid to citric acid. The addition again occurs only *trans*.

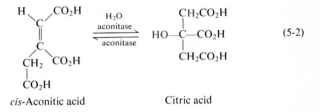

cis-Aconitic acid   Citric acid

The reverse process is equally stereospecific forming only the *cis*-aconitic acid, that is, the isomer with both CO_2H groups attached on the same side of the double bond.

The enzyme-catalyzed hydration of fumaric acid occurs fastest at pH 6.5 (Fig. 5-1).

In the absence of enzyme, the rate of the fumaric acid reaction at this pH has not been equaled even when the reaction was run at 180°C at a pressure of 10 atm. Chemists normally run hydration reactions at more convenient temperatures and at atmospheric pressure by the use of dilute acids as catalysts. The mechanism then is represented as

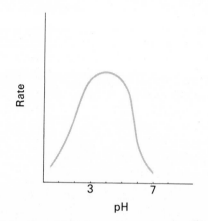

Fig. 5-1. Plot of initial rate of reaction of fumaric acid with water in presence of fumarase in an acetate buffer at 25°C. [C. Frieden and R. A. Alberty, J. Biol. Chem., 212: 859 (1955)].

but an interesting isotope study puts a restriction on this mechanism. When 2-methyl-2-butene is hydrated in D_2O the intermediate carbonium ion (II) is presumably formed.

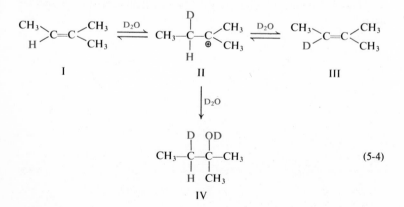

But if the ion is formed rapidly and reversibly some deuterated alkene (III) should form during the reaction. Yet on isolating the alkene after 50% reaction, no deuterated alkene was found (determined by use of a mass spectrograph), suggesting that the breakdown of the ion to form the product (IV) is extremely rapid compared with the re-formation of alkene.

An alternative proposal is analogous to that suggested for bromination, namely that the D (and, therefore, H in the usual hydration) is added symmetrically across the double bond

$$>C=C< \quad \underset{H_2O}{\overset{H_3O^{\oplus}}{\rightleftharpoons}} \quad \left[\overset{H}{\underset{>C-C<}{\overset{\diagup\diagdown}{}}} \right]^{\oplus} \qquad (5\text{-}5)$$

where presumably it is more easily removed than an H covalently bound in a C—H bond. But this mechanism has not been generally accepted.

5-2 ADDITION OF ACIDS [6a,7]

Many acids add to double bonds. The structure of the addition product is predicted by a rule suggested by the Russian chemist W. Markownikov in 1870: The H of an acid, HX, adds to that carbon of an alkene hydrocarbon which already carries the larger number of hydrogens.

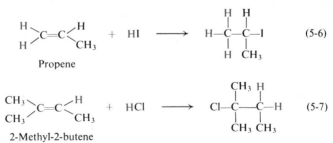

Propene (5-6)

2-Methyl-2-butene (5-7)

Markownikov's rule has been facetiously summarized as "to the carbon that hath shall be given."

The reason for this preference is the fact that the reaction proceeds through a carbonium ion intermediate. Tertiary carbons can carry a positive charge more easily than secondary which can carry them more easily than primary carbons.

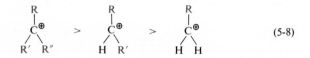

$$(5\text{-}8)$$

Thus of the two possible carbonium ions for Eq. (5-6)

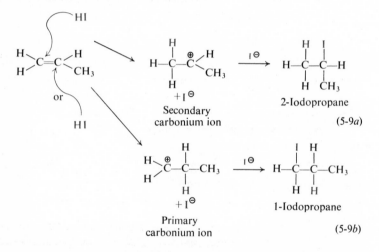

the former is strongly preferred, thus yielding $(CH_3)_2CHI$, 2-iodopropane, rather than $CH_3CH_2CH_2I$, 1-iodopropane.

Why are tertiary carbonium ions more easily formed and more stable? Table 5-1 gives data on the ease of breaking C—H bonds to carbonium ions.

The view widely accepted is that alkyl groups are better than hydrogen atoms in dispersing the positive charge on an adjacent carbon. On the charge cloud picture a bonded hydrogen has a proton embedded within the bonding electron-pair cloud. Thus the pair is likely to be very tightly held and not easily shifted toward a positive center. A carbon—carbon bond, on the other hand, has its bonding pair located between two positive nuclei, each itself surrounded by

Table 5-1   Enthalpies of Formation of Carbonium Ions by the Process R—H → R$^\oplus$ + H· + $e^\ominus$

	ΔH kcal
(CH$_3$)$_3$C—H → (CH$_3$)$_3$C$^\oplus$	262
(CH$_3$)$_2$CH—H → (CH$_3$)$_2$CH$^\oplus$	276
CH$_3$—CH$_2$—H → CH$_3$CH$_2$$^\oplus$	299
CH$_3$—H → $^\oplus$CH$_3$	332

a charge cloud of two electrons. The latter bonding pair is thus likely to be more easily distorted and displaced.

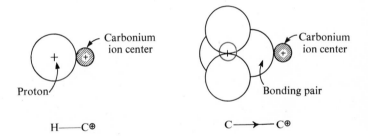

A shift of electrons toward the positive charge reduces the central charge and creates a charge on the alkyl group

Now, it is one thing to conclude that one ion is more stable and quite another to predict that the more stable will be formed much faster. The more stable product may only be reachable by a very high activation energy and in fact some reactions do form the less stable product faster, and subsequently the more stable product is slowly formed.

But in carbonium ion formation, the transition state for a carbonium ion is likely to be stabilized by alkyl groups as well as the final ion, because a partial positive charge is formed as the system approaches the transition-state configuration. The same factors that stabilize a full charge also operate to stabilize a partial charge.

$$
\underset{R}{\overset{R}{>}}C=C\underset{R}{\overset{H}{<}} \xrightarrow{\text{HA}} \quad \overset{R}{\underset{R}{>}}\overset{\delta\oplus}{C}=\!=\!\overset{}{C}\underset{R}{\overset{H}{<}} \qquad (5\text{-}10)
$$

The R groups again can spread out the charge forming on the carbon atom thus making it easier for a charged entity to form.

Whereas most acids (and water) add to alkenes according to the Markownikov rule, the addition of HBr for years was a puzzle to chemists. Sometimes it added according to the rule and sometimes it did not. The puzzle, as we shall see, was solved in 1933 (Sec. 5-4).

5-3 MORE STEREOSPECIFIC ADDITIONS [6a,10b]

One convenient path for the investigation of addition mechanisms is the use of cyclic alkenes. Cyclopentene, for instance, adds two OH groups *cis* if treated with neutral or slightly alkaline potassium permanganate. In the reaction, the purple $KMnO_4$ is reduced to

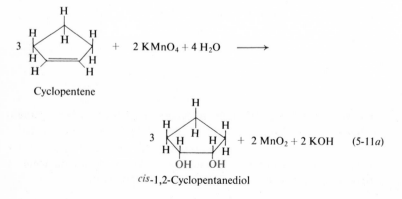

cis-1,2-Cyclopentanediol

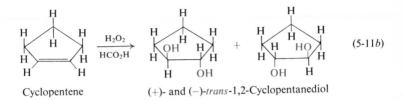

Cyclopentene   (+)- and (−)-*trans*-1,2-Cyclopentanediol

brown manganese dioxide, MnO_2, giving a convenient visual test for alkenes. The two OH groups can be added *trans* by treating with hydrogen peroxide and formic acid at room temperature and then heating with water or $OH^\ominus$ to decompose intermediate products (5-11).

To explain the cis addition when $KMnO_4$ is used, an intermediate is proposed

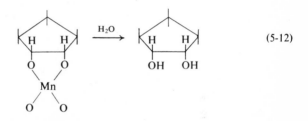

and an analogous structure

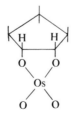

has in fact been isolated as a stable intermediate when osmium tetroxide, OsO_4, reacts with the alkene. The hydrogen peroxide–formic acid process is more complicated. An epoxide, a three-membered oxygen ring, is postulated as an intermediate which is opened at either end by an S_N2 attack of formic acid.

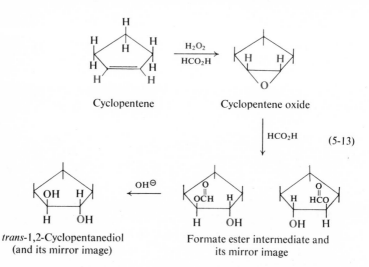

Cyclopentene   Cyclopentene oxide

(5-13)

trans-1,2-Cyclopentanediol
(and its mirror image)

Formate ester intermediate and
its mirror image

5-4 MARKOWNIKOV OPPOSED BY RADICALS [1*b*,6*c*,12]

Until 1933 no one could tell beforehand whether in a particular experiment HBr would follow Markownikov's rule or not.

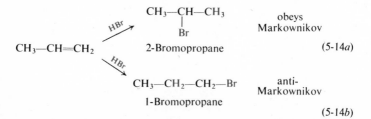

CH_3—CH=CH_2

CH_3—CH—CH_3 | Br obeys Markownikov

2-Bromopropane   (5-14*a*)

CH_3—CH_2—CH_2—Br anti-Markownikov

1-Bromopropane

(5-14*b*)

Light was blamed for the strange behavior, the solvent used, the presence of moisture or its absence. The problem was solved by M. S. Kharasch (University of Chicago) and F. W. Mayo (Stanford Research Institute) reportedly because detailed perusal of a research notebook (which included dates of opening new bottles of alkene) revealed that fresh alkene obeyed Markownikov, while as it aged, the reverse pattern slowly predominated. Anti-Markownikov behavior was traced to exposure to oxygen, which with an alkene forms peroxides, which in turn break down into neutral radicals (fragments containing an odd number of electrons around an atom).

$$\text{Alkene} + O_2 \longrightarrow \text{ROOH} \qquad (5\text{-}15)$$

$$R\text{—}\bar{O} \diagup \bar{O}\text{—}H \xrightarrow{\text{heat or light}} R\text{—}\bar{O}\cdot + \cdot\bar{O}\text{—}H \qquad (5\text{-}16)$$

The two radicals now attack HBr and each has two paths available. In the case of R—O·

$$R\text{—}O\cdot + H \colon \underline{\bar{B}r}\vert \rightarrow R\text{—}O \colon H + \vert \underline{\bar{B}r}\cdot \qquad \Delta H = -23\text{ kcal} \qquad (5\text{-}17)$$

or

$$R\text{—}O\cdot + H \colon \underline{\bar{B}r}\vert \rightarrow R\text{—}O \colon \underline{\bar{B}r}\vert + H\cdot \qquad \Delta H = +39\text{ kcal} \qquad (5\text{-}18)$$

The former path is strongly preferred energetically and a bromine atom becomes available for further reaction. It would gain stability by gaining an electron, and a double bond is a convenient electron source. In the presence of an unsymmetrical alkene, two new paths are now open

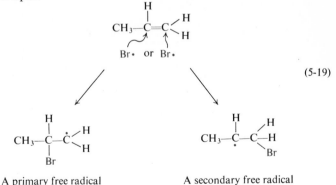

(5-19)

A primary free radical   A secondary free radical

Now, free radical centers, just as carbonium ion centers, are electron deficient. A secondary free radical as before has more carbon—carbon bonds adjacent to the free radical center and the bonds can supply some of the electron density. Secondary free radicals are preferred

and this new radical attacks a second HBr molecule abstracting a hydrogen atom

$$
\begin{array}{ccc}
& \overset{\displaystyle H}{\underset{\displaystyle H\;\;Br}{CH_3-\underset{\bullet}{C}-CH_2Br}} & \longrightarrow \quad \overset{\displaystyle H}{\underset{\displaystyle H}{CH_3-C-CH_2Br}} \quad + Br\cdot
\end{array} \qquad (5\text{-}20)
$$

Thus *n*-propyl bromide is formed, an anti-Markownikov product, and a bromine atom can attack a further molecule by Eq. (5-19). We have here a chain reaction, initiated by a very small amount of peroxide. Occasionally two atoms or radicals meet, terminating the chain

$$A\cdot + B\cdot \;\rightarrow\; A\!-\!B$$

Radicals or atoms

We will meet radical chains again (Sec. 5-8)

5-5 ANTI-MARKOWNIKOV ADDITION BY A FOUR-CENTER REACTION—HYDROBORATION [2]

H. C. Brown (Purdue University) has during the last few years discovered numerous uses of boron compounds in organic synthesis. Although boron is normally considered to have a valence of 3, BH_3 does not exist. Its dimer, diborane, B_2H_6, is known, and complexes with ethers such as with the useful solvent, tetrahydrofuran.

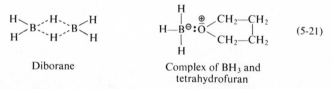

$$(5\text{-}21)$$

Diborane Complex of BH_3 and tetrahydrofuran

Since B_2H_6 and many of its derivatives are spontaneously flammable, the reagent is prepared during the reaction (from sodium borohydride, $NaBH_4$, and boron trifluoride, BF_3) and the alkyl borane product obtained from an alkene is oxidized with alkaline hydrogen peroxide at 25 to 30°C to yield an alcohol. Anti-Markownikov products are always obtained.

$$3 \text{ NaBH}_4 + 4 \text{ BF}_3 \longrightarrow 2 \text{ B}_2\text{H}_6 + 3 \text{ NaBF}_4 \tag{5-22}$$

$$\text{CH}_3\text{CH}{=}\text{CH}_2 \xrightarrow[\text{(2) H}_2\text{O}_2,\text{ OH}^\ominus]{\text{(1) B}_2\text{H}_6} \text{CH}_3\text{CH}_2\text{CH}_2\text{OH} \tag{5-23}$$
Propylene

Three propylenes first link to a boron atom

$$\text{CH}_3\text{CH}{=}\text{CH}_2 \xrightarrow{\text{B}_2\text{H}_6} \text{CH}_3\text{CH}_2\text{CH}_2\text{BH}_2$$
$$\downarrow$$
$$(\text{CH}_3\text{CH}_2\text{CH}_2)_2\text{BH}$$
$$\downarrow$$
$$(\text{CH}_3\text{CH}_2\text{CH}_2)_3\text{B} \tag{5-24}$$

and the tri-1-propylboron is then decomposed by reaction with hydrogen peroxide.

$$(\text{CH}_3\text{CH}_2\text{CH}_2)_3\text{B} + 3 \text{ H}_2\text{O}_2 \xrightarrow{\text{OH}^\ominus} 3 \text{ CH}_3\text{CH}_2\text{CH}_2\text{OH} + \text{B(OH)}_3 \tag{5-25}$$
n-Propyl alcohol   Boric acid

The BH_3 fragment that adds has a deficiency of two electrons and again attacks the double bond in such a way as to create a new electron deficiency at that point where it can be coped with by neighboring alkyl groups most easily. Boron, therefore, adds at the end carbon, forming a partially positive secondary carbon. This carbon then captures a hydrogen from a B—H bond.

$$\text{CH}_3{-}\text{CH}{=}\text{CH}_2 \xrightarrow{\text{B}_2\text{H}_6} \overset{\delta\oplus}{\text{CH}_3{-}\text{CH}}{=}{=}\text{CH}_2 \longrightarrow \text{CH}_3{-}\text{CH}{=}{=}\text{CH}_2$$

$$\begin{array}{cc} & \overset{\delta\ominus}{\text{H}-\text{B}-\text{H}} \qquad\qquad \text{H}\text{-}\text{-}\text{-}\text{-}\text{-}\text{B}\text{-}\text{H} \\ & \text{H} \qquad\qquad\qquad \text{H} \end{array}$$

A four-center
transition state

$$\downarrow$$

$$\begin{array}{cc} \text{CH}_3{-}\text{CH}{-}\text{CH}_2 \\ \text{H} \qquad \text{BH}_2 \end{array} \tag{5-26}$$

Finally, hydroboration always leads to cis addition of water to the double bond

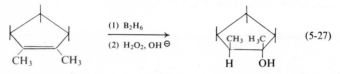

$$\begin{array}{c}\text{(1) } B_2H_6 \\ \xrightarrow{\hspace{2cm}} \\ \text{(2) } H_2O_2, \text{OH}^{\ominus}\end{array}$$

(5-27)

cis-1,2-Dimethylcyclopentene   *cis*-1,2-Dimethylcyclopentanol

This implies that the boron atom is displaced and the OH enters from the same side of the carbon, a reaction opposite to that typical of the S_N2 process.

5-6 ALKYLATION [6a,10a]

Alkylation is the addition of an alkyl group to oxygen, nitrogen, carbon, or other atom. A convenient way to attach an alkyl group to carbon is to add an alkane to an alkene. This only works easily if a carbonium ion intermediate is easily formed, and then the direction of attack is determined by the reagent structures. The aviation fuel "isooctane,"[1] which is really 2,2,4-trimethylpentane, is prepared by reaction of 2-methylpropane with 2-methylpropene

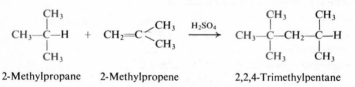

2-Methylpropane   2-Methylpropene   2,2,4-Trimethylpentane

(5-28)

Sulfuric acid protonates the alkene in such a way as to form a tertiary carbonium ion

---

[1] Isooctane was used in the creation of the scale of "octane numbers." Heptane, $CH_3(CH_2)_5CH_3$, was given the octane number zero because it knocked badly, isooctane 100 because it was at the time considered the best fuel.

$$CH_2=C\underset{CH_3}{\overset{CH_3}{\big\langle}} \xrightarrow{H_2SO_4} CH_2\overset{\oplus}{-}C\underset{CH_3}{\overset{CH_3}{\big\langle}} + HSO_4^{\ominus} \qquad (5\text{-}29)$$
$$\underset{H}{\big|}$$

$$\overset{O}{\underset{\substack{| \\ O-H}}{H)-O-S-O}}$$

This carbonium ion attacks another molecule of alkene to form a larger tertiary carbonium ion

$$CH_3-C\overset{\oplus}{\underset{CH_3}{\overset{CH_3}{\big\langle}}} + CH_2=C\underset{CH_3}{\overset{CH_3}{\big\langle}} \longrightarrow$$

$$\underset{\substack{| \\ CH_3}}{\overset{\substack{CH_3 \\ |}}{CH_3-C}}-CH_2-C\overset{\oplus}{\underset{CH_3}{\overset{CH_3}{\big\langle}}} \qquad (5\text{-}30)$$

The new carbonium ion abstracts the tertiary hydrogen of 2-methylpropane as a hydride ion, that is, with its bonding electron pair, the reaction being simply a competition between two carbonium ions for H:$^{\ominus}$. Here the larger cation wins.

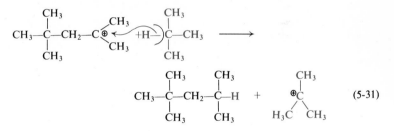

The tertiary butyl cation formed can pursue the same reactions [Eqs. (5-30) and (5-31)] by a continuous chain process.

5-7 CARBONIUM ION REARRANGEMENTS [6b]

Hydride ions are removed not only by external carbonium ions. We saw in Sec. 3-4 that when neopentyl bromide was made to react by an S_N1 mechanism, its rate did not show severe steric hindrance and the products indicated rearrangements. A primary carbonium ion is first formed and either simultaneously or very soon thereafter a methyl group with its bonding electron pair shifts in order that a tertiary carbonium ion may be formed instead.

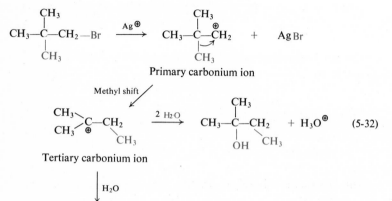

Primary carbonium ion

Tertiary carbonium ion

(5-32)

But we do not need an adjacent methyl group for rearrangements to occur. 1-Butanol treated with sulfuric acid yields mainly 2-butene which is only possible if hydrogen shifts at some stage to the number-1 carbon.

$$\overset{4}{CH_3}\overset{3}{CH_2}\overset{2}{CH_2}\overset{1}{CH_2}OH \xrightarrow{H_2SO_4} CH_3-CH=CH-CH_3 \qquad (5-33)$$

1-Butanol   2-Butene

The primary carbonium ion formed by loss of water

$$CH_3CH_2CH_2CH_2OH \xrightarrow{H_2SO_4} CH_3CH_2CH_2CH_2\overset{\oplus}{O}H + \overset{\ominus}{O}SO_3H$$
$$\qquad\qquad\qquad\qquad\qquad\qquad\qquad | \qquad\qquad$$
$$\qquad\qquad\qquad\qquad\qquad\qquad\qquad H \qquad\qquad$$

$$CH_3CH_2CH_2CH_2\overset{\oplus}{O}H \longrightarrow CH_3CH_2-\overset{H}{\underset{H}{C}}-C\overset{H}{\underset{H}{\oplus}} + H_2O \qquad (5-34)$$

rearranges to the more stable secondary carbonium ion by a hydride ion shift

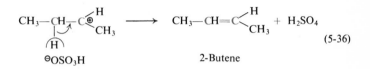

$$(5-35)$$

The new carbonium ion loses a proton to form 2-butene as the main product

$$CH_3—CH—C\overset{H}{\underset{CH_3}{\diagup}}^{\oplus} \quad \longrightarrow \quad CH_3—CH{=}C\overset{H}{\underset{CH_3}{\diagup}} \; + \; H_2SO_4$$

$$\underset{2\text{-Butene}}{}$$

$$(5-36)$$

$$^{\ominus}OSO_3H$$

The 1-butanol → 2-butene reaction is a dehydration, a loss of water, occurring with rearrangement. When structures are suitable no rearrangement is necessary or observed.

$$\begin{matrix} CH_3 \\ CH_3{-}C{-}C{-}H \\ HO \quad H \end{matrix} \xrightarrow{H_2SO_4} \begin{matrix} CH_3 \\ {>}C{=}CH_2 \\ CH_3 \end{matrix}$$

$$+ \; H_3O^{\oplus}$$
$$+ \; OSO_3H^{\ominus}$$

$$(5-37)$$

2-Methyl-2-propanol   2-Methylpropene

This alkene formation from alcohols is the reverse of the hydration processes discussed in Sec. 5-1. Fumarase catalyzes both the hydration of fumaric acid and the dehydration of (−)-malic acid, speeding the attainment of equilibrium from either side.

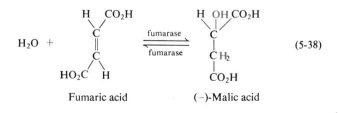

$$(5-38)$$

Fumaric acid   (−)-Malic acid

5-8 ISOPRENE, GALLSTONES AND RUBBER [7,11b]

Isoprene, or 2-methyl-1,3-butadiene,

$$CH_2=C\underset{CH=CH_2}{\overset{CH_3}{<}}$$

is obtained when natural rubber is heated and distilled. Isoprene's molecular formula is C_5H_8 and that of rubber is $(C_5H_8)_n$, with n in the range of 1,000 to 5,000. It looks as if isoprene is the *monomer* of the *polymer* rubber, that isoprene is the building block of which rubber is made. Determination of the structure of rubber has confirmed this.

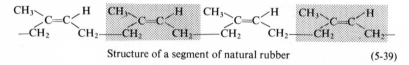

Structure of a segment of natural rubber   (5-39)

The parts of the isoprene molecule have customarily been labeled with a head and a tail as well as the usual numbers along the chain

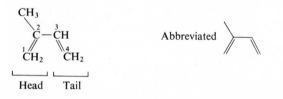

The isoprene units in natural rubber appear to have three characteristics:

(*a*) They are *all* linked at 1,4 positions

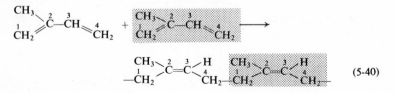

(5-40)

When Br_2 adds to the parent compound, 1,3-butadiene, we obtain mostly 1,4-addition but about a fifth of the product is the result of 1,2-addition.

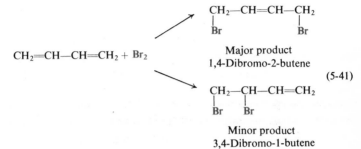

$$CH_2=CH-CH=CH_2 + Br_2$$

$$CH_2-CH=CH-CH_2$$
$$\quad | \qquad\qquad\qquad |$$
$$Br \qquad\qquad\qquad Br$$

Major product
1,4-Dibromo-2-butene

$$CH_2-CH-CH=CH_2$$
$$\quad | \quad\; |$$
$$Br \quad Br$$

Minor product
3,4-Dibromo-1-butene

(5-41)

In natural rubber no 1,2-linking of isoprene units has been detected.

(*b*) Isoprene units are all linked head-to-tail

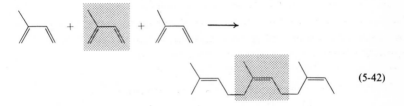

(5-42)

No head-head or tail-tail junctions have been observed.

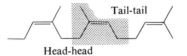

(*c*) The product is all *cis* around each double bond, that is, the two branches of the polymer proceed from the same side of the double bond

$$\text{ww}-CH_2 \overset{CH_3}{\diagdown} C=C \overset{H}{\diagup} CH_2-\text{ww}$$

all-*cis*: Natural rubber

Another natural product, gutta-percha, which lacks rubber's elastic properties, is an all *trans* polyisoprene.

$$
\begin{array}{c}
CH_3 \diagdown \qquad \diagup CH_2\text{---}\!\!\backsim\!\!\backsim \\
\qquad C\!\!=\!\!C \\
\!\!\backsim\!\!\backsim\text{---}CH_2 \diagup \qquad \diagdown H
\end{array}
$$

all-*trans*: Gutta-percha

When isoprene is heated, a sticky mess is obtained consisting of 1,2- and 1,4-addition product; head-head, tail-tail, and head-tail junctions; and *cis* and *trans* configurations around the double bond. A more common polymerization procedure, heating with oxygen or peroxides under pressure, yielded similar unsatisfactory results.

tert-Butyl peroxide, $(CH_3)_3C\text{---}O\text{---}O\text{---}C(CH_3)_3$, on heating breaks symmetrically into two neutral radicals which can initiate polymerization in alkenes. With ethylene, polyethylene is formed.

Initiation:

$$(CH_3)_3C\text{---}\underline{\bar{O}}\!:\!\underline{\bar{O}}\text{---}C(CH_3)_3 \;\rightarrow\; (CH_3)_3C\text{---}\underline{\bar{O}}\cdot \;+\; \cdot\underline{\bar{O}}\text{---}C(CH_3)_3 \qquad (5\text{-}43)$$

Propagation:

$$RO\cdot + H_2C\overset{\cdot\cdot}{\text{---}}CH_2 \;\rightarrow\; RO\!:\!CH_2\text{---}\overset{\bullet}{C}H_2$$

Ethylene

$$RO\text{---}CH_2\text{---}\overset{\bullet}{C}H_2 + CH_2\!\!=\!\!CH_2 \;\rightarrow\; RO\text{---}CH_2\text{---}CH_2\!:\!CH_2\text{---}\overset{\bullet}{C}H_2 \text{ etc.} \qquad (5\text{-}44)$$

Termination:

(*a*) By combination of two radicals

$$RO\text{---}CH_2\text{---}(CH_2)_n\text{---}\overset{\bullet}{C}H_2 \quad + \quad \overset{\bullet}{C}H_2\text{---}(CH_2)_m\text{---}CH_2\text{---}OR$$

$$\downarrow$$

$$RO\text{---}CH_2\text{---}(CH_2)_{(m+n+2)}\text{---}CH_2\text{---}OR \qquad\qquad (5\text{-}45)$$

(*b*) By chain transfer. The growing radical picks a hydrogen atom off another polymer chain or radical, thus initiating a new radical chain on another molecule.

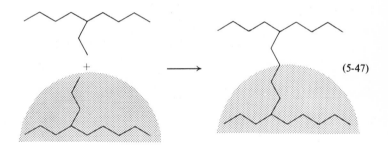

$$RO—CH_2—(CH_2)_n—\overset{\displaystyle .}{C}H_2 + \text{\Large ⋁⋀}—CH_2—CH—CH_2—\text{\Large ⋁⋀}$$

$$RO—CH_2—(CH_2)_n—CH_2 + \text{\Large ⋁⋀}—CH_2—\underset{\displaystyle .}{C}H—CH_2—\text{\Large ⋁⋀}$$

(5-46)

The new radical will now grow a chain from its middle and is quite likely to form a cross-link with another branching chain.

(5-47)

Now the difference between an unbranched polymer and a cross-linked one is that the former will melt on heating—it is *thermoplastic*— and can, therefore, be formed by molding. The plastic material can be heated and poured into the desired mold. A cross-linked polymer, on the other hand, cannot wriggle significantly more when hot than cold. It is a *thermosetting* plastic like Bakelite, from which telephones are usually made. The polymer must be prepared (and cross-linked) in the mold, since once formed it is almost impossible to alter its shape—except destructively.

When a radical initiates the polymerization of isoprene

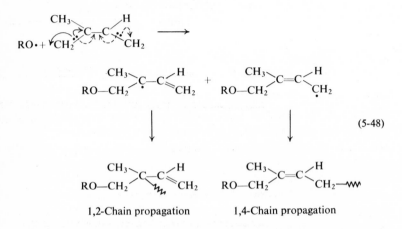

1,2-Chain propagation   1,4-Chain propagation

1,2 and 1,4 adducts, *cis* and *trans*, cross-linked and non-cross-linked molecules result and the product is a most inhomogeneous mass.

Natural rubber as obtained from rubber trees was of course useless for tires. Not being cross-linked it melted on warming—an unhappy prospect for a summer day. That problem was solved by Charles Goodyear in 1839 by creating cross-links of the same kind as were later found in cross-linked protein chains—bridges of sulfur atoms. Vulcanization, the heating of rubber with sulfur creates sulfur cross-links.

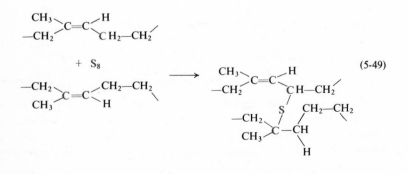

In proteins, cysteine residues carry sulfhydryl groups, SH, which on oxidation create similar sulfur bridges.

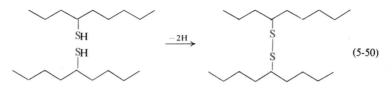

$$(5\text{-}50)$$

During the 1950s new polymerization catalysts were developed by Karl Ziegler (Max Planck Institute for Coal Research) and Giulio Natta (Polytechnic Institute of Milan) which led to extremely uniform products. Whereas metallic sodium gives the usual kind of mixture, finely divided metallic lithium was one of the successful catalysts. Another was a complex of triethylaluminum and titanium tetrachloride. Using these new catalysts isoprene was polymerized to what has become known as synthetic natural rubber, a 1,4, head-to-tail, *cis*-configuration polymer indistinguishable from natural rubber. One explanation for this stereospecificity as each isoprene unit is added, is that the new unit attaches at the connecting point between growing chain and catalyst after arranging itself on the catalyst surface.

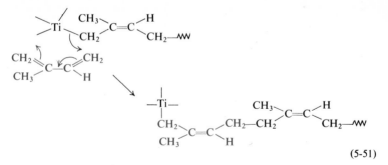

$$(5\text{-}51)$$

Isoprene is not only the unit of rubber and gutta-percha. The five-carbon unit, attached to others usually in a head-to-tail manner, appears in numerous chemicals extracted from natural products particularly in plants.

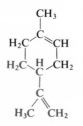

Limonene found in the oils of lemon and orange and in pine needles.

The racemic, ±, mixture can be prepared from isoprene by heating to about 300°C.

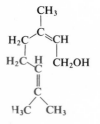

Geraniol from oil of geranium

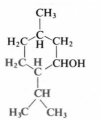

Menthol from oil of peppermint

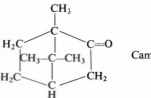

Camphor

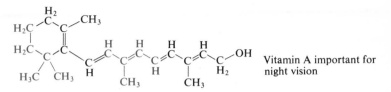

Vitamin A important for night vision

The head-to-tail attachment of isoprene units has appeared so often that it became a guiding principle for structural elucidation in natural products. Of several possibilities, that structure was chosen that followed the "isoprene rule" of head-to-tail attachment. This has occasionally led to error. The coloring matter of carrots, β-carotene, can be seen to be related to two vitamin-A structures by a tail-to-tail linkage of isoprene units at the center.

Tail-tail linkage

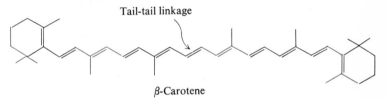

β-Carotene

5-9 THE BIOSYNTHESIS OF CHOLESTEROL [4,5,8,9,11a]

In recent years biochemical studies of the synthesis of cholesterol (the major constituent of gallstones) and of steroid hormones have shown that these two are built largely from isoprene units and that isoprene itself is constructed from acetic acid by reaction with co-enzyme A, the coenzyme which in the Krebs cycle (Sec. 5-1) helps break down fats by removing two carbons at a time and converting them to carbon dioxide. Since the coenzyme A molecule carries a sulfhydryl group through which it links to the acetic acid molecule, it is usually abbreviated as CoASH.

$$CH_3-\overset{O}{\overset{\|}{C}}-OH + CoASH \longrightarrow CH_3\overset{O}{\overset{\|}{C}}-SCoA \qquad (5\text{-}52)$$

Acetyl coenzyme A

Three of the acetyl coenzyme A molecules combine to form a six-carbon hydroxyacid, mevalonic acid, which picks up phosphate groups from adenosine triphosphate (a nucleotide) to form isopent-3-enyl pyrophosphate, known as the biological isoprene unit.

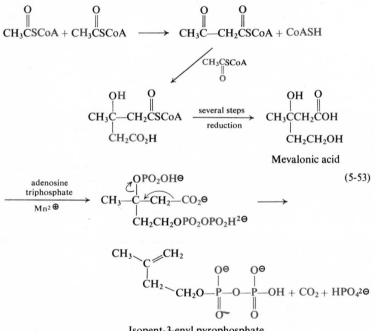

(5-53)

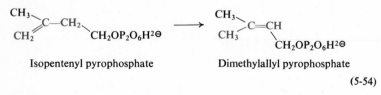

Isopent-3-enyl pyrophosphate

The isopentenyl pyrophosphate is believed to be isomerized enzymatically to dimethylallyl pyrophosphate

Isopentenyl pyrophosphate   Dimethylallyl pyrophosphate

(5-54)

which easily ionizes because it forms an allylic (CH_2—CH=CH_2

is the allyl group) carbonium ion stabilized by resonance
$[\overset{\oplus}{C}H_2-CH=CH_2, CH_2=CH-\overset{\oplus}{C}H_2]$.

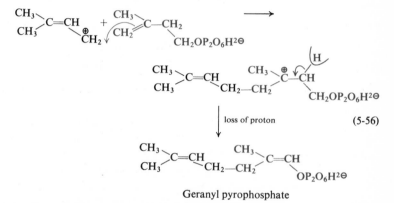

$$(5\text{-}55)$$

The carbonium ion now attacks a second isopentenyl pyrophosphate head-to-tail and the isoprene construction process is on its way.

$$(5\text{-}56)$$

Geranyl pyrophosphate

By the use of radioactive carbon, ^{14}C, the fate of acetic acid in metabolism can be traced. By labeling first the methyl group of acetic acid $^{14}CH_3CO_2H$, and then the carboxyl group $CH_3{}^{14}CO_2H$, feeding the acid as its sodium salt to an animal and isolating cholesterol from it, every carbon in the cholesterol molecule has been shown to derive from one or the other carbon of acetic acid.

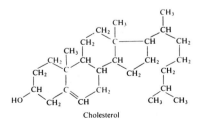

Cholesterol

Fragments of the cholesterol molecule are removed and their activity determined. If we abbreviate acetic acid, CH_3—CO_2H, as m-c (m = methyl carbon, c = carboxyl carbon) the origins of the cholesterol carbons may be designated as follows:

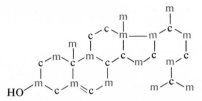

Its biosynthesis is believed to occur by way of squalene which is synthesized by the isoprene construction sequence already described. Labeled squalene has been converted to labeled cholesterol by homogenized liver tissue. The most fascinating step of the proposed mechanism is the "zippering up" of a long chain into the four rings also contained in cholesterol.

$$(CH_3)_2C=CHCH_2CH_2\underset{\underset{CH_3}{|}}{C}=CHCH_2CH_2\underset{\underset{CH_3}{|}}{C}=CHCH_2CH_2CH=\underset{\underset{CH_3}{|}}{C}CH_2CH_2CH=\underset{\underset{CH_3}{|}}{C}CH_2CH_2CH=C(CH_3)_2$$

Squalene

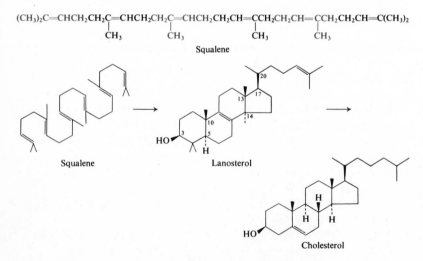

Squalene   Lanosterol

Cholesterol

Although squalene contains no asymmetric carbon atoms, the biosynthesis of lanosterol produces a compound with seven asymmetric carbon atoms (at positions 3, 5, 10, 13, 14, 17, 20). Thus

$2^7 = 128$ isomers could be formed but only one is produced. Figure 5-2 shows the proposed cyclization process for the conversion of squalene-2,3-oxide, which in 1966 was shown to be an intermediate in the biosynthesis of cholesterol, into cholesterol's tetracyclic ring system.

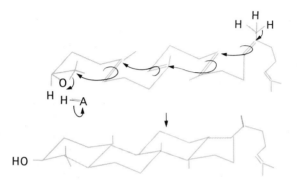

Fig. 5-2. Cyclization of squalene-2,3-oxide. [After W. S. Johnson, Accounts Chem. Res., 1:1 (1968).]

SUGGESTED READINGS

1. Breslow, R. G.: "Organic Reaction Mechanisms," (*a*) chap. 4; (*b*) chap. 7, W. A. Benjamin Co., New York, 1965.
2. Brown, H. C.: "Hydroboration," W. A. Benjamin Co., New York, 1962.
3. Bruice, T. C., and S. J. Benkovic: "Bioorganic Mechanisms," vol. I, chap. 4, W. A. Benjamin Co., New York, 1966.
4. Clayton, R. B.: Biosynthesis of Sterols, Steroids and Terpenoids, *Quart. Rev.*, **19**:168 (1965).
5. Cornforth, J. W.: Exploration of Enzyme Mechanisms by Asymmetric Labelling, *Quart. Rev.*, **23**:125 (1969).
6. Hine, J.: "Physical Organic Chemistry," 2d ed., (*a*) chap. 9; (*b*) chap. 14; (*c*) chap. 20, McGraw-Hill Book Company, New York, 1962.

7. Ingold, C. K.: "Structure and Mechanism in Organic Chemistry," chap. 12, Cornell University Press, Ithaca, N.Y., 1953.

8. Johnson, W. S.: Non-enzymic Biogenetic-like Olefinic Cyclizations, *Accounts Chem. Res.*, **1**:1 (1968).

9. Mahler, H. R., and E. H. Cordes: "Biological Chemistry," chap. 15, Harper & Row, Publishers, Incorporated, New York, 1966.

10. Morrison, R. J., and R. N. Boyd: "Organic Chemistry," 2d ed., (*a*) chap. 6; (*b*) chaps. 6, 28, Allyn & Bacon, Inc., Boston, 1966.

11. Richards, J. H., D. J. Cram, and G. S. Hammond: "Elements of Organic Chemistry," (*a*) chap. 23; (*b*) chaps. 23, 24, McGraw-Hill Book Company, New York, 1967.

12. Walling, C.: "Free Radicals in Solution," John Wiley & Sons, Inc., New York, 1957.

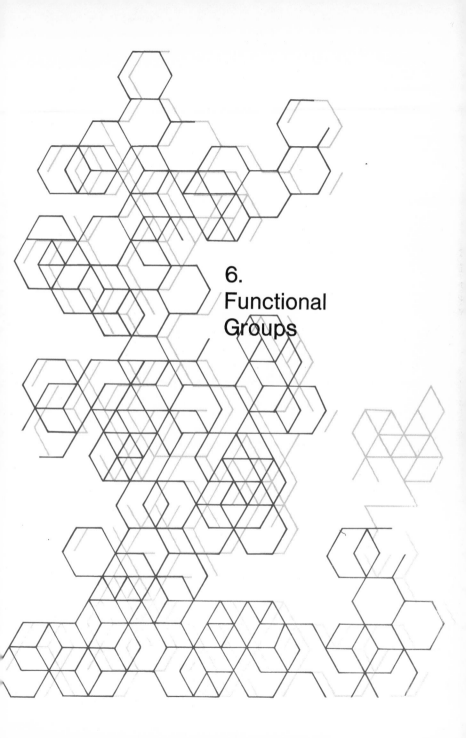

6.
Functional
Groups

6-1 INTRODUCTION [7]

An enzyme could not act as a catalyst for a given reaction if on its surface at specific locations were not situated groups of atoms that can perform particular functions. These groups have become known as functional groups and they seem to behave—within the limits we will discuss further in this chapter—as independent entities, that is, independent of what else is in the molecule. An —OH group behaves in similar ways in numerous compounds which have been given the collective name of alcohols. Only when the —OH group is adjacent to another functional group (such as C=O or a second —OH), or when two functional groups are ideally located for a special task (such as ring formation), or when many groups of the same kind are present in a molecule (as —OH groups in sugar) are significant deviations from the usual behavior of —OH expected.

The discovery of the principle of independence of functional groups in the 1830s marked the decisive turning point in the rational development of organic chemistry. Until then, organic chemistry, in F. Wöhler's (1800–1882 Professor at Göttingen, Germany) expressive phrase, was a jungle. Functional groups provided a way out. It was hoped that they were to organic compounds what elements were to inorganic ones, that there would be a limited number of functional groups, and that these would have a rational order to them as elements had a pattern—expressed later in the periodic table. But functional groups kept on being discovered and we now do not believe there is a limit to them. The simplest ones can be organized according to the periodic table, according to the principal valence of the atom attached to carbon (Table 6-1).

Groups in Sec. *A* of the table, containing single bonds only, yield compounds that often cannot easily be added to. Almost all reactions of these compounds are by substitution at the carbon atom [normally of one functional group by another (see Sec. 2-3)], or by elimination to form multiple bonds (Sec. 5-7).

Groups in Sec. *B* can undergo addition reactions at their double bond. We have discussed so far additions to C=C bonds only. Triple-bond mechanisms generally follow the double-bond mechanism

Table 6-1 Table of Simple Functional Groups

Periodic table group of central atom	4	5	6	7
A. Groups attached to carbon by single bonds		$-NH_2$	$-OH$	$-F$
		$>NH$	Alcohols	Alkyl fluorides
		$\geq N$	$>O$	
		Primary, secondary, and tertiary amines	Ethers	
		$-PH_2$	$-SH$	$-Cl$
		$>PH$	Thiols	Alkyl chlorides
		$\geq P$	$>S$	
		Phosphines	Thioethers	$-Br$
				Alkyl bromides
				$-I$
				Alkyl iodides
B. Groups with double bonds to carbon				
	$>C=C<$	$>C=N-$	$>C=O$	
	Alkenes	Imines	Aldehydes, RCHO, and ketones, R_2CO	
C. Groups with triple bonds to carbon				
	$-C\equiv C-$	$-C\equiv N$		
	Alkynes	Nitriles		

twice over but sometimes involve complications. Acetylene adds two moles of Br_2:

Propyne, $CH_3—C\equiv CH$, on the other hand, on adding water, seems to obey Markownikov's rule twice, but the *gem*-diol (*gem* is short for gemini = twin)

$$\left[\begin{array}{c} CH_3—C—CH_3 \\ HO \quad OH \end{array} \right] \xrightarrow{\text{loss of } H_2O} CH_3—C—CH_3$$

A *gem*-diol (never found)   Acetone—a ketone

we would expect has never been obtained (even by treating CH_3CCH_3 with Cl Cl

with hydroxide ion) because two OH groups on the same carbon are most unstable, giving a ketone (in this case acetone) instead. In fact, propyne almost certainly adds H_2O only once to form another structure never isolated, an unsaturated alcohol (or enol) which presumably rearranges very rapidly to its ketone isomer, acetone (we will meet enols again in Sec. 6-6). Propyne does add two bromine

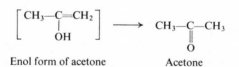

Enol form of acetone   Acetone

molecules forming $CH_3CBr_2CHBr_2$, and two HBr molecules according to Markownikov's rule (in the absence of air or peroxides) to give $CH_3CBr_2CH_3$. Sometimes the reaction can be stopped after the addition of just one molecule of reagent and in this way the stereospecificity of hydrogenation reagents has been discovered. Whereas sodium in liquid ammonia adds H_2 *trans*, a nickel-boride catalyst discovered by H. C. Brown (Sec. 5-5) and his son C. A. Brown, adds H_2 *cis*.

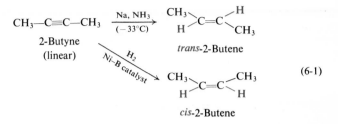

(6-1)

It is believed that a hydrogen molecule attaches itself to the Ni—B catalyst surface, partially or completely breaking its H—H bond.

$$H_2 + M—M—M—M—M \rightarrow M—M—M—M—M$$

The alkyne's multiple bond then comes close to the two hydrogens and reacts with them. By a similar means, over a nickel catalyst, Sabatier and Senderens developed the basis of the commercial oleomargarine industry, the hydrogenation of oils to fats.

$$
\begin{array}{l}
CH_3(CH_2)_7CH{=}CH(CH_2)_7CO_2CH_2 \\
CH_3(CH_2)_7CH{=}CH(CH_2)_7CO_2CH \\
CH_3(CH_2)_7CH{=}CH(CH_2)_7CO_2CH_2
\end{array}
\xrightarrow[\text{Ni catalyst}]{3\,H_2}
\begin{array}{l}
CH_3(CH_2)_{16}CO_2CH_2 \\
CH_3(CH_2)_{16}CO_2CH \\
CH_3(CH_2)_{16}CO_2CH_2
\end{array}
$$

(6-2)

Triolein (all *cis*) (found in olive oil)   Tristearin (found in beef fat)

In the citric acid cycle, the opposite occurs; succinic acid in the presence of the enzyme succinate dehydrogenase removes two hydrogens to form the *trans* isomer, fumaric acid, only. Its *cis* isomer, maleic acid, is never formed in this reaction.

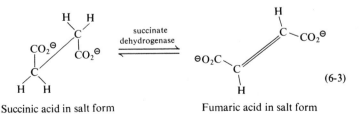

(6-3)

Succinic acid in salt form   Fumaric acid in salt form

This dehydrogenation has been shown to be *trans*, suggesting an ionic mechanism with a cyclic intermediate.

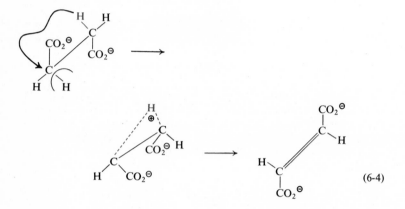

(6-4)

6-2 THE CARBONYL GROUP $\gtrsim$C=O [2,3b,13]

The most important functional group not yet discussed in detail is the double bond between carbon and oxygen. It is found as part of more complex functional groups in proteins and fats, and plays an important role in the ring-opening mechanism of carbohydrates (Sec. 4-7). One unusually large ring compound found in nature and containing the $\gtrsim$C=O group is muscone, a perfume component obtained from the male musk deer.

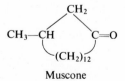

Muscone

If we compare the electronegativity, that is, the electron-attracting power, of carbon and oxygen we should not be surprised to find that it is higher for oxygen than for carbon. In the series of isoelectronic molecules, that is, molecules containing the same number of electrons, and of nuclei other than hydrogen,

$$
\begin{array}{cccc}
\overset{\textstyle H}{\underset{\textstyle H}{H\!:\!\ddot{C}\!:\!H}} & \overset{}{\underset{\textstyle H}{H\!:\!\ddot{N}\!:\!H}} & \overset{}{\underset{\textstyle H}{:\!\ddot{O}\!:\!H}} & :\!\ddot{\underset{\cdot\cdot}{F}}\!:\!H \\
+6 & +7 & +8 & +9
\end{array}
$$

Nuclear charges on heavy atom

we can expect electrons between the central nucleus and a proton to be most strongly attracted by F and least by C. Thus of the bonds C—H, N—H, O—H, F—H, the fluorine—hydrogen bond will be most polarized $\overset{\delta\ominus}{F} \!\!\leftarrow\!\! \overset{\delta\oplus}{H}$, the C—H bond least. Thus H—F is an acid in water,

$$
H\!-\!\bar{\underset{\textstyle H}{O}}\!\mid + \; H\!\!\Big)\!\!-\!\bar{\underset{\cdot\cdot}{F}}\!\mid \longrightarrow H\!-\!\overset{\oplus}{\underset{\textstyle H}{O}}\!-\!H + \mid\bar{\underset{\cdot\cdot}{F}}\!\mid^{\ominus}
$$

and water donates a proton to ammonia forming some $OH^{\ominus}$ ion

$$
H\!-\!\overset{\textstyle H}{\underset{\textstyle H}{N}}\!\mid + \; H\!\!\Big)\!\!-\!\bar{O}\!\mid \rightleftharpoons H\!-\!\overset{\textstyle H}{\underset{\textstyle H}{\overset{\oplus}{N}}}\!-\!H + \mid\bar{\underset{\textstyle H}{O}}\!\mid^{\ominus}
$$

If we replace one H in the above series by CH_3 we obtain another isoelectronic series

CH_3—CH_3	CH_3—NH_2	CH_3—OH	CH_3—F
Ethane	Methylamine	Methanol	Methyl fluoride

Here methanol acts as a proton donor to methylamine.

$$
CH_3\!-\!\overset{\textstyle H}{\underset{\textstyle H}{N}}\!\mid + \; H\!\!\Big)\!\!-\!\bar{\underset{\textstyle CH_3}{O}}\!\mid \rightleftharpoons CH_3\!-\!\overset{\textstyle H}{\underset{\textstyle H}{\overset{\oplus}{N}}}\!-\!H + \mid\bar{\underset{\textstyle CH_3}{O}}\!\mid^{\ominus}
$$

Methylammonium methoxide

Oxygen is again more electronegative than carbon, so that, whereas $CH_3—CH_3$ is a symmetric nonpolar molecule, the C—O bond in methanol is polarized $\overset{\delta\oplus}{C}H_3—\overset{\delta\ominus}{O}H$. We come to the same conclusion in the doubly bonded series

$$H_2C{=}CH_2 \qquad\qquad H_2C{=}NH \qquad\qquad H_2C{=}O$$

or more generally in the sequence

$$\underset{\text{Alkene}}{{>}C{=}CH_2} \qquad\qquad \underset{\text{Imine}}{{>}C{=}\ddot{N}H} \qquad\qquad \underset{\text{Aldehyde or ketone}}{{>}C{=}\ddot{O}}$$

The oxygen having a higher nuclear charge than carbon will have a greater attraction for electrons

$${>}\overset{\delta\oplus}{C}{=}\overset{\delta\ominus}{\underset{\text{}}{O}}$$

In our discussion of the C=C double bond we found that the common reagents, Br_2, HBr, and H_2SO_4 attack as electrophilic reagents—that is, a positively charged fragment ($Br^\oplus$, $H^\oplus$) of the reagent becomes attached to one of the electron pairs of the double bond. In the case of the carbonyl group, the oxygen atom in a sense acts as the electrophilic or electron-seeking body and the more usual reagents are nucleophilic—they seek a nucleus to which the unshared electron pair that they bring with them can bond. A simple example is the reaction of acetaldehyde with ammonia to form an unstable adduct.

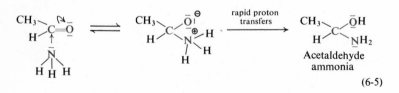

(6-5)

With hydrazine, H_2NNH_2, the addition product is seldom isolated because it loses water to yield a C=N double bond.

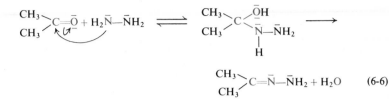

$$(6\text{-}6)$$

Acetone hydrazone

The hydrazone is stabilized by delocalization of the electron pair of the end nitrogen.

This and similar reactions of substituted ammonia molecules with carbonyl compounds are accelerated by very low concentrations of acid but slowed down by higher concentrations.

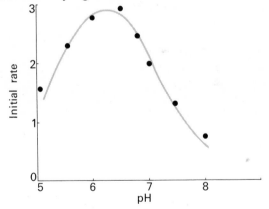

Fig. 6-1. Variation of reaction rate with pH in reaction of carbonyl compounds with substituted ammonias.

Acids protonate carbonyl groups,

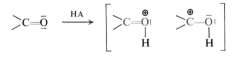

Table 6-2 Rates of Semicarbazone Formation, Enthalpies and Entropies of Activation, at 0.03° C and pH 7

	Rate constant k at 0.03°C	Enthalpy of activation $\Delta H^{\ddagger}$ kcal	Difference in entropy of activation $\Delta S^{\ddagger} - \Delta S^{\ddagger}_{\text{acetone}}$ entropy units, cal/deg mole
Acetone $H_3C-C-CH_3$, O	63.5×10^{-3}	2.0	0.0
Pinacolone $H_3C-C-C-CH_3$, CH_3, CH_3, O	0.771×10^{-3}	1.8	−9.7
Cyclopentanone	8.26×10^{-3}	4.0	3.3
Cyclohexanone	437×10^{-3}	1.1	0.4

Source: F. P. Price, Jr., and L. P. Hammett, *J. Am. Chem. Soc.*, **63:** 2387 (1941).

thus further withdrawing electrons from carbon and facilitating attack on carbon by a nucleophilic reagent. But acids also protonate and, therefore, inactivate the unshared electron pair which is needed for nucleophilic attack

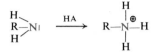

This is the energetically favored location for protons, but due to random collisions some will also find themselves on the carbonyl compound. Thus a maximum rate at a weakly acid concentration is to be expected.

Enthalpies and entropies of activation for the reaction of ketones with semicarbazide, $NH_2NHCONH_2$, as the ketone structure is varied, are given in Table 6-2.

The reaction appears to involve a rate-determining addition of semicarbazide to the $C=O$ group, followed by dehydration of the resulting intermediate adduct.

$$\underset{R}{\overset{CH_3}{>}}C=O + NH_2NHCONH_2 \rightleftharpoons \underset{R}{\overset{CH_3}{>}}C\underset{NHNH-C-NH_2}{\overset{OH}{<}} \longrightarrow$$

$$\underset{R}{\overset{CH_3}{>}}C=NNHCNH_2 + H_2O \quad (6\text{-}7)$$

R = CH_3 (acetone)
R = C(CH_3)_3 (pinacolone)

The 80-fold decrease in rate from acetone to pinacolone is seen to be due almost solely to a decrease in the entropy of activation, the activation enthalpy remaining essentially unchanged.

Now the entropy of activation is the difference between the entropy of the starting materials (ketone, semicarbazide, and solvent system) and the entropy of the transition state of the rate-determining step. The latter will have considerable tetrahedral character around the central carbon atom. Thus we assume that the $—C(CH_3)_3$ group had considerably more freedom in the relatively uncrowded pinacolone

Pinacolone

than in the crowded transition state of reaction. Hence the large negative value for $\Delta S^{\ddagger} - \Delta S^{\ddagger}_{\text{acetone}}$.

The startling difference in reactivity between cyclopentanone (one-eighth that of acetone) and cyclohexanone (seven times faster than acetone) is explainable in terms of a similar change to a tetrahedral transition state. The chair form of cyclohexane

can accommodate all neighboring bonds in staggered positions where these interfere least with each other

Staggered conformation   Eclipsed conformation
Minimum repulsion   Maximum repulsion

Cyclohexanone, on the other hand, cannot fit its $\diagup C{=}O$ group into a staggered location. The transition state is like the staggered cyclohexane structure and is, therefore, formed easily—due to a lowered enthalpy of activation. Cyclopentane has almost a completely eclipsed conformation and so does the transition state.

Cyclopentane

Cyclopentanone has its C=O group in the plane of the ring where it interferes less with neighboring C—H bonds

Thus cyclopentanone requires a large enthalpy of activation to reach a tetrahedral transition state.

6-3 ADDITION OF WATER TO CARBONYL COMPOUNDS
[3*b*,5*b*]

At 20°C, formaldehyde is 99.99% hydrated in pure water

$$\begin{array}{ccc} \underset{H}{\overset{H}{\diagdown}}\text{C=O} + H_2O & \longrightarrow & \underset{H}{\overset{H}{\diagdown}}\text{C}\underset{OH}{\overset{OH}{\diagup}} \\ \text{Formaldehyde} & & 99.99\% \end{array} \tag{6-8}$$

acetaldehyde, CH_3CHO, is 58% hydrated, while the extent of hydration of acetone at equilibrium is very small. These figures were obtained from ultraviolet spectroscopy and nuclear magnetic resonance data.

Using $H_2^{18}O$, M. Cohn and H. C. Urey showed that oxygen exchange with acetone and, therefore, presumably hydration of acetone

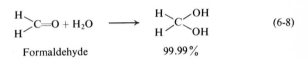

is slow in pure water but is strongly accelerated by acids and bases. Since formaldehyde is hydrated rapidly even in pure water, water must act as a sufficiently strong acid or base catalyst for that reaction. The methyl groups of acetaldehyde and acetone help to stabilize the C=O group by sending electrons toward the positive carbon. This

$$\underset{CH_3}{\overset{CH_3}{\diagdown}}\text{C}\overset{\delta\oplus}{=}\underset{}{\overset{\delta\ominus}{\underline{O}}}$$

carbon is thereby made less positive and hence less susceptible to attack by nucleophilic reagents. Water will no longer be effective but $OH^{\ominus}$ will. In acid, protonation of oxygen will put a much larger $\oplus$ charge on the adjacent carbon enhancing its reactivity toward water.

When electron-withdrawing groups are close to the carbonyl group, stable crystalline hydrates can be isolated. In this case, the positive charge on the carbonyl carbon is increased.

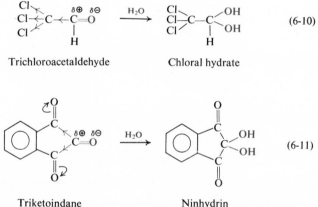

Trichloroacetaldehyde   Chloral hydrate (6-10)

Triketoindane

Ninhydrin
A color reagent for amino acids (6-11)

6-4 THE ADDITION OF ALCOHOLS [3b]

Aldehydes in alcohol solution form an equilibrium with a hemiacetal addition compound.

$$CH_3-C\overset{H}{\underset{O}{\diagdown}} + C_2H_5OH \rightleftharpoons CH_3-\overset{\overset{\displaystyle H}{|}}{\underset{\underset{\displaystyle OH}{|}}{C}}-OC_2H_5 \quad (6\text{-}12)$$

In the presence of dry HCl or other strong acid, a second step becomes possible and an acetal is formed, by way of a stabilized positive ion.

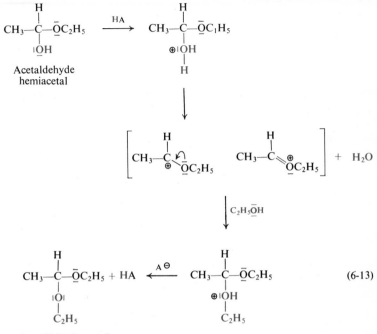

Acetaldehyde
hemiacetal

Acetaldehyde acetal

(6-13)

In the mutarotation of glucose (Sec. 4-7) the hemiacetal ring form was much more stable than the aldehyde form, whereas with acetaldehyde the opposite is the case. This is almost certainly an entropy effect. The formation of acetaldehyde hemiacetal reduces the freedom of two molecules. In glucose both groups are already part of the same molecule and the six-membered ring acetal forms with little crowding or strain.

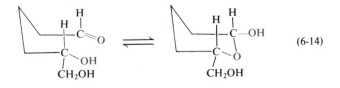

(6-14)

6-5 ALDOL CONDENSATION [2,3*b*,5*b*,9*c*]

In the presence of base or acid, acetaldehyde will act as nucleophilic reagent at the carbonyl group of a second acetaldehyde molecule. Due to resonance, a hydrogen on a carbon adjacent to a carbonyl group has considerable acidic properties. Bromination occurs at this point as we have seen (Sec. 2-2). The removal of a proton at this location allows the negative charge on carbon to be spread on to the carbonyl oxygen.

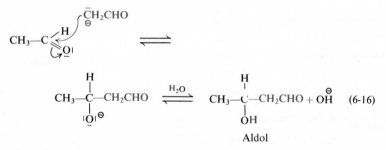

$$(6\text{-}15)$$

The resulting carbanion can attack a carbonyl carbon.

$$(6\text{-}16)$$

Aldol

The product is aldol, and the reaction is known as an *aldol condensation.*

The reaction occurs as long as "α-hydrogens" (H on C adjacent to C=O) are available. Thus aldol can react with a further acetaldehyde molecule. Or acetaldehyde can react with an aldehyde or ketone that does not have an α-hydrogen, to form a "mixed aldol condensation."

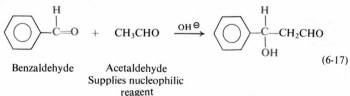

$$(6\text{-}17)$$

Benzaldehyde   Acetaldehyde
                    Supplies nucleophilic
                         reagent

The product readily loses water because thereby a conjugated system—-alternating single and double bonds—is formed, allowing for charge delocalization and greater stability.

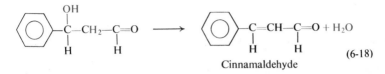

Cinnamaldehyde

(6-18)

Aldol, which lacks the benzene ring's added contribution to the conjugated system, will lose water only on heating or in the presence of an acid. Of the two possible products, the one that is formed preponderantly is the one with a conjugated system of bonds.

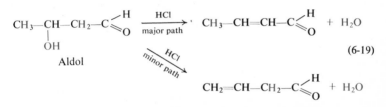

(6-19)

We can now see why acetaldehyde and benzaldehyde in the presence of base give preponderant yields of cinnamaldehyde with almost no contamination by aldol. Formation of aldol is an easily reversible reaction while the dehydration to produce cinnamaldehyde has a very high reverse activation energy. The latter, therefore, does not hydrate again.

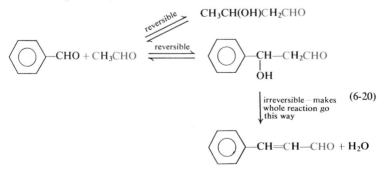

(6-20)

6-6 TAUTOMERISM, ENOLIZATION, INTERNAL ALDOL CONDENSATION [3a,4,5a,8]

Kekulé, as we have seen (Sec. 1-8), had been worried about the failure to discover two 1,2-dibromobenzenes. This failure of the original structural theory was met by development of the theory of resonance. A second group of substances, each of which seemed to correspond to more than one structural formula, had a very different conceptual history. The most famous example is ethyl acetoacetate, with molecular formula $C_6H_{10}O_3$. Everyone agreed that it was an ethyl ester, so that the formula was developed to read

$$C_3H_5O-\underset{\underset{O}{\|}}{C}OC_2H_5$$

where the arrangement of atoms in the C_3H_5O part was unknown. It was first prepared by A. Geuther in 1863 by treatment of ethyl acetate with sodium (and a trace of ethanol to yield some sodium ethoxide, $2\ Na + 2\ C_2H_5OH \rightarrow 2\ C_2H_5O^{\ominus}Na^{\oplus} + H_2$).

$$CH_3\underset{\underset{O}{\|}}{C}OC_2H_5 + CH_3\underset{\underset{O}{\|}}{C}OC_2H_5 \xrightarrow{C_2H_5O^{\ominus}Na^{\oplus}} C_3H_5O-\underset{\underset{O}{\|}}{C}OC_2H_5 + C_2H_5OH$$

(6-21)

Geuther discovered that the product of the reaction formed a crystal-line sodium salt, $C_6H_9O_3Na$ when neutralized with bases. The sodium salt with ethyl iodide formed an ethyl derivative, just as the sodium salts of alcohols do ($RO^{\ominus}Na^{\oplus} + C_2H_5I \rightarrow ROC_2H_5 + Na^{\oplus} + I^{\ominus}$; see Sec. 2-3). Ethyl acetoacetate also added a molecule of Br_2.

Because ethyl acetoacetate could be alkylated like an alcohol and reacted with bromine, Geuther proposed the enol (*en* for the $C{=}C$ double bond, *ol* for OH group) structure.

$$CH_3-\underset{\underset{HO}{|}}{C}{=}\underset{\underset{H}{|}}{C}-\underset{\underset{O}{\|}}{C}-OC_2H_5$$

Enol formula

Four years later E. Frankland and B. F. Duppa reported reactions of ethyl acetoacetate typical of a ketone

$$C-C-C$$
$$\overset{||}{\underset{O}{}}$$

group. It reacted with substituted ammonias such as hydroxylamine, NH_2OH, and phenylhydrazine, $C_6H_5NHNH_2$. They proposed that ethyl acetoacetate was not an enol but rather had a ketonic structure

$$CH_3-\overset{||}{\underset{O}{C}}-CH_2-\overset{||}{\underset{O}{C}}-OC_2H_5$$

Keto formula

After some controversy between the backers of the two formulas, and similar controversies in the case of other compounds, Conrad Laar in 1885 pointed out that a very small shift in the position of a hydrogen atom can convert one into the other.

$$CH_3-\overset{\overset{H}{|}}{C}=\overset{}{\underset{\underset{O-H}{}}{C}}-CO_2C_2H_5 \quad \rightleftharpoons \quad CH_3-\overset{\overset{H}{|}}{\underset{O}{C}}-\overset{}{\underset{H}{C}}-CO_2C_2H_5 \quad (6\text{-}22)$$

He therefore proposed a rapid transfer of hydrogen between the two positions, so that removal of either the keto or enol form by reaction with a suitable reagent would shift the equilibrium and allow the reaction to go to completion.

The phenomenon of a seemingly single substance behaving as two became known as *tautomerism* and the term is now reserved for situations where the presence of two substances has been established or is strongly suspected.

In 1911 L. Knorr and K. H. Meyer independently obtained two forms of ethyl acetoacetate, corresponding to the keto and enol formulas previously suggested. Clearly if there is a rapid equilibrium between two forms, then their interconversion could probably be slowed down by lowering the temperature if a significant enthalpy of activation, ΔH^+, exists. Knorr separated the solid keto form by cooling a concentrated solution of the ester in a hydrocarbon solvent to dry ice temperature (solid CO_2 at $-78°C$). The keto crystals melted at $-39°C$, reacted only slowly with Br_2 and gave no color with ferric chloride, $FeCl_3$, a typical reagent for the C=C—OH group. When the sodium salt of the ester in the same solvent at $-78°C$ was treated with gaseous HCl, an oil separated, reacting rapidly with Br_2 and giving an immediate red color with $FeCl_3$. This form was concluded to be the enol.

In the absence of base or acid, the two forms remain unchanged for long periods at $-78°C$. In quartz (SiO_2) containers, they remain unchanged at room temperature and even can be distilled, but in ordinary glass vessels at room temperature, each rapidly reverts to the same equilibrium mixture. This strange behavior has been traced to the slightly basic character of glass. The tautomeric equilibrium is in fact base- or acid-catalyzed and is extremely slow in the absence of catalyst. A trace of hydroxide ion is sufficient. Ethyl acetoacetate has two weakly acidic α-hydrogens and the removal of one by base leaves a strongly stabilized carbanion because of two adjacent C=O groups.

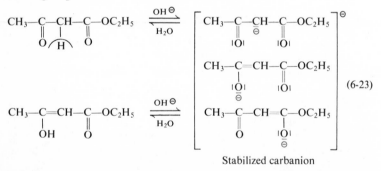

(6-23)

Stabilized carbanion

This sequence of reactions indicates the essential difference between tautomerism and resonance stabilization. When two structures can be written differing in the atoms linked (that is, H linked to O or C), then both forms exist. When structures differ only in electron distribution, as in the carbanion, then only a single substance exists whose structure corresponds to a superposition of all the contributing structures.

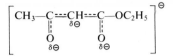

$$\left[CH_3{-}\underset{\underset{\underset{\delta\ominus}{O}}{\|}}{C}{=\!=\!=}\underset{\delta\ominus}{CH}{=\!=\!=}\underset{\underset{\delta\ominus}{O}}{\overset{}{\underset{\|}{C}}}{-}OC_2H_5 \right]^{\ominus}$$

Carbanion of ethyl acetoacetate

It might be asked why the proton does not add to the doubly bonded ester oxygen. But this would form a hemiacetal, a much less stable possibility than the keto or enol forms.

$$CH_3{-}\underset{\underset{O}{\|}}{C}{-}CH{=}\underset{\underset{OH}{|}}{C}{-}OC_2H_5$$

Hemiacetal form of ethyl acetoacetate

Since bromination of enol is fast and of keto form slow, percent of enol form in the equilibrium mixture can be determined. Spectroscopic methods have also been used.

Table 6-3   Percent of Enol in Keto-Enol Tautomers at Equilibrium

	Keto form	*Enol form*	*Enol %*
Acetone	$CH_3{-}\overset{O}{\overset{\|}{C}}{-}CH_3$	$CH_3{-}\overset{OH}{\overset{\|}{C}}{=}CH_2$	0.00025
Ethyl acetoacetate	$CH_3{-}\overset{O}{\overset{\|}{C}}{-}\overset{O}{\underset{H_2}{C}}{-}\overset{O}{\overset{\|}{C}}{-}OC_2H_5$	$CH_3{-}\overset{OH}{\overset{\|}{C}}{=}\overset{}{\underset{H}{C}}{-}\overset{O}{\overset{\|}{C}}{-}OC_2H_5$	7.5
Acetylacetone	$CH_3{-}\overset{O}{\overset{\|}{C}}{-}\overset{}{\underset{H_2}{C}}{-}\overset{O}{\overset{\|}{C}}{-}CH_3$	$CH_3{-}\overset{OH}{\overset{\|}{C}}{=}\overset{}{\underset{H}{C}}{-}\overset{O}{\overset{\|}{C}}{-}CH_3$	80
Biacetyl	$CH_3{-}\overset{O}{\overset{\|}{C}}{-}\underset{\underset{O}{\|}}{C}{-}CH_3$	$CH_2{=}\overset{OH}{\overset{\|}{C}}{-}\underset{\underset{O}{\|}}{C}{-}CH_3$	0.0056

The low percent of enol in acetone and biacetyl is due to the fact that the negative charge in the carbanion can only be spread onto one neighboring oxgyen. Both ethyl acetoacetate and acetylacetone can offer two carbonyl oxygens for charge delocalization and a keto C=O group is evidently more effective than the C=O group of an ester linkage $CO_2C_2H_5$. The enol forms of both these structures are stabilized by hydrogen bonding—weak bonds between oxygen-linked hydrogens and nonbonded oxygens.

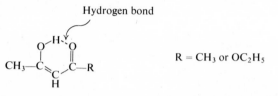

R = CH_3 or OC_2H_5

This stabilization is particularly strong in six-membered rings because no angle distortions are necessary. A strong resemblance is evident when tautomerism and an aldol condensation are compared. In fact the former can be seen to be simply an internal aldol condensation.

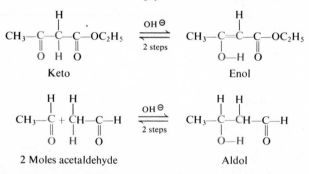

If enolization endows a molecule with aromatic character, the keto form is unlikely to be found.

Phenol   Keto form of phenol
                          Unknown

The enzyme aldolase catalyzes the synthesis of fructose from dihydroxyacetone and glyceraldehyde. The former supplies the carbanion and the latter the carbonyl group. This reaction occurs in the synthesis of glucose in green plants, the conversion from fructose to glucose occurring through an enolization process. The reaction path is believed to be the following:

(*a*) Formation of a carbanion

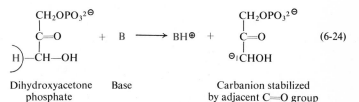

$$(6\text{-}24)$$

Dihydroxyacetone   Base   Carbanion stabilized
phosphate   by adjacent C=O group

(*b*) Aldol condensation

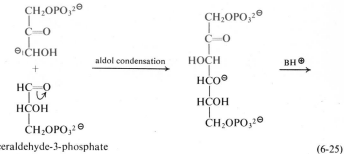

Glyceraldehyde-3-phosphate

$$(6\text{-}25)$$

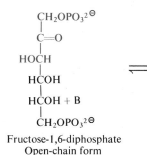

Fructose-1,6-diphosphate
Open-chain form

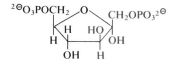

Fructose-1,6-diphosphate
Ring form

(*c*) Conversion of fructose to glucose via an enediol intermediate: The fructose first loses a phosphate group to adenosine diphosphate (ADP) which thereby is converted to adenosine triphosphate (ATP).

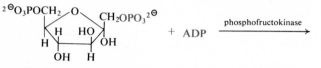

Fructose-1,6-diphosphate

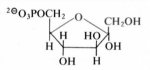

Fructose-6-phosphate $\qquad$ + ATP $\qquad$ (6-26)

The fructose-6-phosphate then reaches an equilibrium with glucose-6-phosphate.

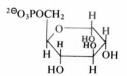

Glucose-6-phosphate

(6-27)

A mechanism for this isomerization has been proposed by Rose, involving enolization of the keto group, present in the open-chain form of fructose, and of the aldehyde group in the open-chain form of glucose (Fig. 6-2).

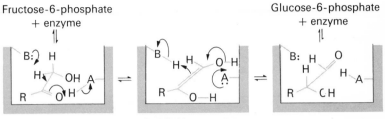

Fructose-6-phosphate + enzyme

Glucose-6-phosphate + enzyme

Enediol intermediate

*Fig. 6-2. Mechanism of isomerization of fructose-6-phosphate to glucose-6-phosphate involving enolization to an "enediol" intermediate on the enzyme surface. [After H. R. Mahler and E. H. Cordes, "Biological Chemistry," p. 421, Harper & Row, Publishers, Incorporated, New York, 1966. Cf. I. A. Rose, Brookhaven Symp. Biol., **15**: 293 (1962).]*

6-7 ALKYLATION OF CARBANIONS [9d]

The sodium salt of ethyl acetoacetate should be a powerful nucleophilic reagent and this is found to be the case. It reacts readily with alkyl halides.

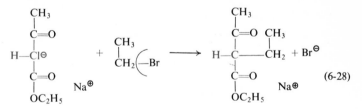

$$(6\text{-}28)$$

The product has a second acidic hydrogen which can be removed by base. Then a second alkyl group can be attached.

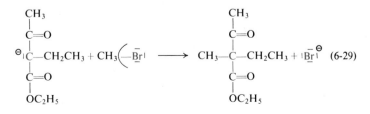

$$(6\text{-}29)$$

This is an important method for introducing alkyl groups adjacent to carbonyl. The product can be modified further in a number of ways (Sec. 6-11).

Acetoacetic acid in combination with coenzyme A appears near the termination of the biodegradation of fats. In normal metabolism it breaks down into two acetyl coenzyme A molecules

$$CH_3COCH_2COSCoA \xrightarrow{HSCoA} 2\ CH_3COSCoA$$

but in diabetics free acetoacetic acid accumulates.

$$CH_3COCH_2COSCoA \xrightarrow{H_2O} CH_3COCH_2CO_2H$$
$$\text{Acetoacetic acid}$$

6-8 COMPLEX FUNCTIONS [16]

C=O + OH — Carboxylic Acids

Both carbonyl and hydroxyl functions are significantly modified when they are directly attached to each other to give the carboxylic acid group.

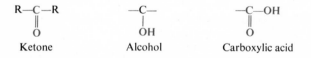

R—C—R ‖ O	—C— | OH	—C—OH ‖ O
Ketone	Alcohol	Carboxylic acid

The most startling property is the acidic character of the group, noticeable by the ability of carboxylic acids to turn blue litmus paper red and change many other indicators to their acid color. The acid ionization constant K_a for the reaction

$$HA + H_2O \rightleftharpoons H_3O^{\oplus} + A^{\ominus} \qquad K_a = \frac{[H_3O^{\oplus}][A^{\ominus}]}{[HA]}$$

is given for a number of substances in Table 6-4.

The effect of the C=O group is startlingly apparent in the change of acid ionization constant from 10^{-18} to 10^{-5} in changing from

Table 6-4 Acid Ionization Constants K_a

Compound		K_a
Formic acid	$H-C{\overset{O}{\underset{O-H}{}}}$	17.7×10^{-5}
Acetic acid	$CH_3-C{\overset{O}{\underset{O-H}{}}}$	1.75×10^{-5}
Chloroacetic acid	$ClCH_2-C{\overset{O}{\underset{O-H}{}}}$	136×10^{-5}
Methane	H_3C-H	10^{-58}
Acetone	$CH_3-\overset{\overset{H}{\mid}}{\underset{\underset{O\ \ H}{}}{C}}-\overset{\mid}{C}-H$	10^{-20}
Acetylacetone	$CH_3-C{\overset{O}{}}$ $HC-H$ $CH_3-C{\underset{O}{}}$	10^{-9}
Ethyl acetoacetate	$CH_3-C{\overset{O}{}}$ $HC-H$ $C_2H_5O-C{\underset{O}{}}$	10^{-10}
Ammonia	H_2N-H	10^{-36}
Ethanol	CH_3CH_2-O-H	10^{-18}
Methanol	CH_3-O-H	10^{-16}
Carbonic acid	$O=C{\overset{O-H}{\underset{O-H}{}}}$	4.3×10^{-7}
Phenol	$\langle\bigcirc\rangle-O-H$	10^{-10}

ethanol, CH_3CH_2OH, to acetic acid, $CH_3\overset{\|}{\underset{O}{C}}OH$. The simple replace-

ment of 2H's by O seems to make all the difference. If $C{=}O$ and OH are separated by a CH_2 group, the ionization constant reverts to the low value typical of an alcohol.

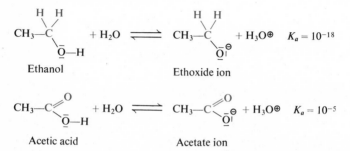

Ethanol   Ethoxide ion $K_a = 10^{-18}$

Acetic acid   Acetate ion $K_a = 10^{-5}$

What an adjacent $C{=}O$ group can do is to offer an alternative and equally stable site for the negative charge on the acetate ion.

$$\left[CH_3{-}C{\overset{\bar{O}}{\underset{\underset{\ominus}{\bar{O}|}}{\diagup}}} \qquad CH_3{-}C{\overset{\overset{\ominus}{\bar{O}|}}{\underset{\bar{O}|}{\diagup}}} \right] = CH_3{-}C{\overset{\overset{\frac{1}{2}\ominus}{\bar{O}|}}{\underset{\underset{\frac{1}{2}\ominus}{\bar{O}|}}{\diagup}}}$$

Resonance forms   Acetate ion

Since both resonance forms are equally stable, they contribute equally to the actual structure. The negative charge is spread evenly over both oxygens, thus greatly stabilizing the ion. An analogous electron redistribution is available to the acetic acid molecule

$$\left[CH_3{-}C{\overset{\bar{O}|}{\underset{\bar{O}{-}H}{\diagup}}} \qquad CH_3{-}C{\overset{\overset{\ominus}{\bar{O}|}}{\underset{\overset{\oplus}{O}{-}H}{\diagup}}} \right] = CH_3{-}C{\overset{\overset{\delta\ominus}{\bar{O}|}}{\underset{\underset{\delta\oplus}{O}{-}H}{\diagup}}}$$

but here, to change from the first to the second resonance form requires the creation and separation of opposite charges. Hence the actual form is much closer to the first resonance form and resonance stabilization is not large. Finally no second forms of significant stability can be written for ethanol and the ethoxide ion. We therefore conclude that acetic acid is stabilized by resonance relative to ethanol, but the acetate ion is stabilized much more relative to the ethoxide ion. The energy relationships are shown in Fig. 6-3.

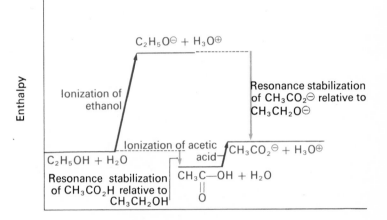

Ionization paths

Fig. 6-3.   Energy relationships for the ionization of ethanol and acetic acid.

6-9 REACTIONS OF CO₂H GROUP TO FORM OTHER COMPLEX FUNCTIONAL GROUPS [2,3c,9b]

The —C—OH group has one major advantage as a reagent over the —CH₂OH group. The former only has three atoms attached to carbon, whereas the latter has four. Since carbon almost never exceeds four covalent bonds attached to it, the approach of a new bonding group to a saturated carbon can only succeed if another group is loosened and displaced. The carboxylic acid group on the other hand can *add* a fourth group, and though this adduct is seldom stable, its formation as an intermediate often facilitates reaction. Carboxylic acids with alcohols form esters, and with ammonia (and amines, RNH_2 or R_2NH) form amides.

$$R-\underset{\underset{O}{\|}}{C}OH + R'OH \rightleftharpoons R-\underset{\underset{O}{\|}}{C}-OR' + H_2O$$

$$R-\underset{\underset{O}{\|}}{C}-OH + NH_3 \rightleftharpoons R-\underset{\underset{O}{\|}}{C}-NH_2 + H_2O$$

In both cases an addition–dissociation mechanism is a common one.

Esterification and Hydrolysis

Fats and oils are commonly encountered biological esters. But even for a simple one such as ethyl propionate, a number of possible mechanisms for its reactions suggest themselves. We might first ask which bonds break when water is eliminated from an acid and alcohol molecule to form an ester—does the OH group come from acid or alcohol?

$$CH_3-\underset{\underset{O}{\|}}{C}-OH + H-OC_2H_5 \rightleftharpoons CH_3-\underset{\underset{O}{\|}}{C}-OC_2H_5 + H_2O \qquad (6\text{-}30)$$

Acyl oxygen fission (acyl = $R-\underset{\underset{O}{\|}}{C}$ group)

or

$$CH_3-\underset{\underset{O}{\|}}{C}-O-H + HO-C_2H_5 \rightleftharpoons CH_3-\underset{\underset{O}{\|}}{C}-OC_2H_5 + H_2O \qquad (6\text{-}31)$$

Alkyl oxygen fission (oxygen bonded to alkyl group breaks)

Curiously it is the reverse reaction, hydrolysis of esters, that has been studied much more systematically. But since a favorable transition state for the reverse reaction implies a favorable transition state for the forward reaction, the data for either direction are useful.

Ethyl propionate labeled with heavy oxygen was shown to cleave at the acyl-oxygen bond in the presence of base.

$$C_2H_5-\underset{\underset{O}{\|}}{C}(-{}^{18}OC_2H_5 + H_2O \underset{}{\overset{OH^\ominus}{\rightleftharpoons}} C_2H_5-\underset{\underset{O}{\|}}{C}-OH + H{}^{18}OC_2H_5$$

(6-32)

$$\overset{OH^\ominus}{\searrow}$$

$$C_2H_5-\underset{\underset{O}{\|}}{C}-O^\ominus + H_2O$$

Acyl-oxygen fission is by far the most frequently encountered mechanism of acid or ester substitution. Only when an alkyl group R attached to the acyl oxygen, $-\underset{\underset{}{}}{\overset{\overset{O}{\|}}{C}}-O-R$, is extremely stable as a carbonium ion, is alkyl-oxygen fission found. This has been observed when R is a *tert*-butyl group, $(CH_3)_3C-$, or a triphenylmethyl group, $(C_6H_5)_3C-$.

Next we can ask what evidence there is for prior addition of an attacking reagent to the carbonyl group before any other group leaves. Myron Bender (Northwestern University) has supplied convincing evidence. In basic hydrolysis (also known as saponification because the sodium salts of long chain carboxylic acids are soaps) a concerted substitution process would not involve ${}^{18}O$ in the carbonyl group.

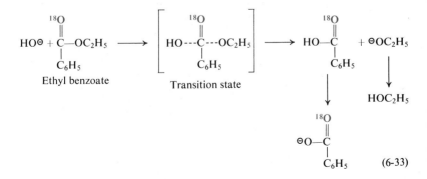

Ethyl benzoate   Transition state

(6-33)

If prior addition of hydroxide ion occurred, rapid proton transfer should make the two oxygens equivalent, and some ^{18}O would be lost from the ester, even without any reaction to acid occurring.

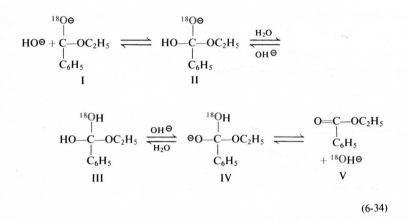

$$(6\text{-}34)$$

In addition to the above equilibria, II and IV can lose $^{\ominus}OC_2H_5$ to form benzoic acid containing ^{18}O.

$$(6\text{-}35)$$

Actually ^{18}O was lost from the ester (and acid). This can only happen in the step from IV to V, and therefore requires the prior addition step.

The ^{18}O is also lost in the acid-catalyzed hydrolysis of esters, again confirming the addition-dissociation mechanism. (Try this on your own and compare your mechanism with that of Prob. 6-1.)

Problem 6-1

Loss of ^{18}O in acid-catalyzed hydrolysis of esters:

Answer

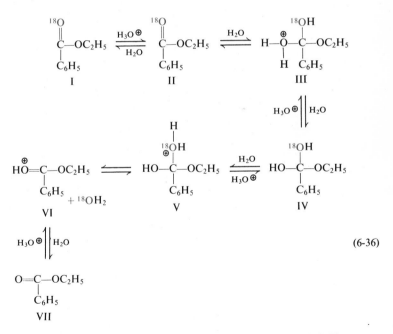

$$(6\text{-}36)$$

The intermediate IV is also protonated at the $-OC_2H_5$ group and splits off C_2H_5OH to yield benzoic acid.

The concerted mechanism again would lead to no ^{18}O loss:

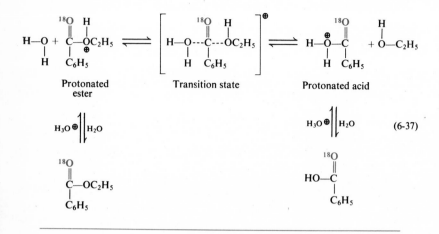

(6-37)

In the small intestine, the hydrolysis of fats and oils is catalyzed by two types of lipases, one to hydrolyze ester groups at the end carbons of glycerol, the other at the middle carbon.

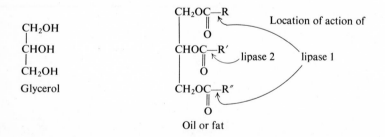

These enzymes appear to be specific for the ester linkage and its location on the glycerol chain but not with regard to the carbon chain groups R, R', and R".

An Alternative Mechanism for Acyl-oxygen Fission

2,4,6-Trimethylbenzoic acid is very hard to esterify in dilute acid under conditions in which benzoic acid easily forms esters.

Benzoic acid   Methyl benzoate

(6-38)

$$CH_3-\langle\bigcirc\rangle-C\overset{O}{\underset{O-H}{\diagdown}} + CH_3OH \underset{}{\overset{dil.\ HCl}{\rightleftharpoons}} \text{ no or very slow reaction}$$

2,4,6-Trimethylbenzoic acid

If, however, 2,4,6-trimethylbenzoic acid is first dissolved in concentrated sulfuric acid, and the mixture poured into cold methanol, the ester product is obtained without difficulty. A clue to the reason for this bizarre behavior is obtained from the freezing point of the sulfuric acid solution (cf. Sec. 1-9). The freezing-point lowering is four times that expected if the benzoic acid merely dissolved without further reaction. The only reasonable mechanism yielding a fourfold depression is

$$(CH_3)_3C_6H_2-C\overset{O}{\underset{O-H}{\diagdown}} + H_2SO_4 \longrightarrow (CH_3)_3C_6H_2-C\overset{O}{\underset{\overset{\oplus}{O}-H}{\diagdown}} + HSO_4^{\ominus}$$
$$\underset{H}{|}$$

$$(CH_3)_3C_6H_2-C\overset{O}{\underset{\overset{\oplus}{O}-H}{\diagdown}} \longrightarrow (CH_3)_3C_6H_2-\overset{\oplus}{C}=O + H_2O$$
$$\underset{H}{|}$$

$$H_2O + H_2SO_4 \longrightarrow H_3O^{\oplus} + HSO_4^{\ominus}$$

Overall equation:

$$(CH_3)_3C_6H_2CO_2H + 2\ H_2SO_4 \rightarrow (CH_3)_3C_6H_2-\overset{\oplus}{C}=O + H_3O^{\oplus} + 2\ HSO_4^{\ominus}$$

(6-39)

Here each acid molecule dissolved yields four particles. On pouring into cold methanol the ester then forms.

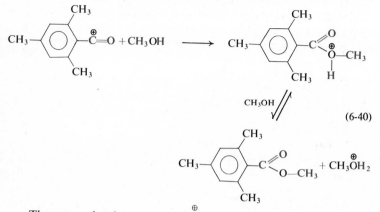

(6-40)

The oxocarbonium ion, $R-\overset{\oplus}{C}=O$, forms only in a strongly acid environment. The slow esterification of the trimethylbenzoic acid in dilute HCl is presumed to be due to steric hindrance by neighboring methyl groups toward the approaching methanol molecule.

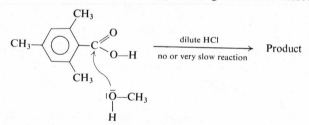

Prior cleavage avoids the steric hindrance.

Strangely enough, benzoic acid,

treated with sulfuric acid and then cold methanol does not yield the ester. Nor does 2, 4, 6-tribromobenzoic acid, suggesting that electrical factors also help determine the ease of formation of the $\overset{\oplus}{R}CO$ ion.

Amide Formation and Hydrolysis

Bender has shown that ^{18}O was lost from benzamide, $C_6H_5CONH_2$, five times as fast as it hydrolyzed, suggesting again a carbonyl-addition intermediate. The hydrolysis is usually first order in amide and first order in base.

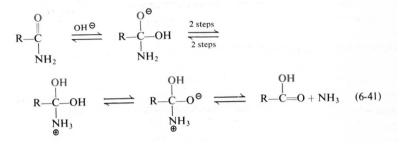

$$R—\overset{OH}{\underset{NH_3}{\underset{\oplus}{|}}}—OH \rightleftharpoons R—\overset{OH}{\underset{NH_3}{\underset{\oplus}{|}}}—O^{\ominus} \rightleftharpoons R—\overset{OH}{\underset{}{|}}—=O + NH_3 \qquad (6\text{-}41)$$

A number of other intermediates are possible also, and it is not clear which are energetically preferred. The amide linkage,

is, of course, the peptide link joining amino acids in protein chains and diamines and dicarboxylic acids in nylon.

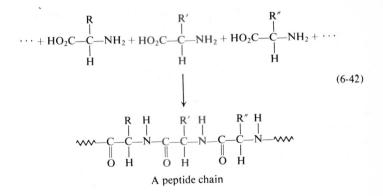

$$(6\text{-}42)$$

A peptide chain

$$\cdots + H_2N(CH_2)_6NH_2 + HO_2C(CH_2)_4CO_2H + H_2N(CH_2)_6NH_2 + \cdots$$

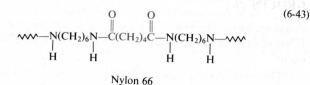

(6-43)

Nylon 66

A model for the enzymatic catalysis of protein hydrolysis and formation was developed by Bender who showed that phthalamic acid, at pH 3.0, is hydrolyzed 100,000 times faster than benzamide, $C_6H_5CONH_2$, both hydrolysis rates being catalyzed by acids. The convenient location of an acid group within the phthalamic acid molecule seems to act as an enormously effective catalyst for the amide hydrolysis. The proposed mechanism involving internal nucleophilic attack (II → III) is as follows:

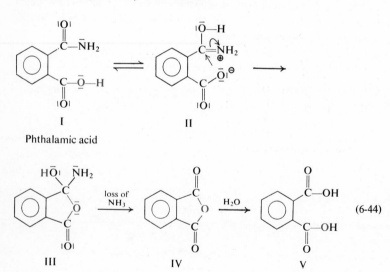

(6-44)

6-10 INTRAMOLECULAR INTERACTION OF FUNCTIONAL GROUPS [9e]

Esters are formed by loss of water between an OH and a CO_2H group. If both groups are in the same molecule, internal ester formation may occur.

However, if the two functional groups are attached to adjacent carbons, the acid-catalyzed dehydration does not involve the CO_2H group at all.

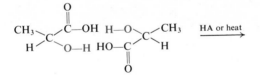

$$R—CH—CH—CO_2H \xrightarrow[\text{heat}]{\text{HA}} R—CH{=}CH—CO_2H + H_2O \quad (6\text{-}45)$$

Instead, an α,β-unsaturated acid is the major product because the C=C bond is conjugated with C=O.

If both functional groups are attached to the same carbon, acids or heat link two molecules of the α-hydroxy acid forming a six-membered ring containing two ester groups.

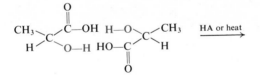

α-Hydroxypropionic acid

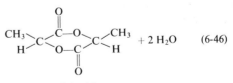

Propiolactide

When OH and CO_2H groups are separated by two or three carbons, water is lost between the two groups of the same molecule forming five-membered or six-membered internal esters, or lactones, with little bending of bonds from their lowest energy locations.

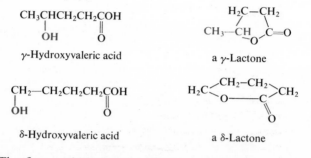

The five- and six-membered oxygen-containing rings are the fundamental ring structures of most sugars—fructose has a five-membered and glucose a six-membered oxygen ring.

To form a four-membered ring is not impossible but molecules tend to take alternative reaction paths if available, because these small rings involve angle strain and crowding. Crowding also accounts for the relative sparsity of seven- and eight-membered rings even though no distortions from tetrahedral angles would be necessary if atoms were point particles. Since OH and CO_2H can form ester linkages between *two* molecules as well as one, polymers can be formed.

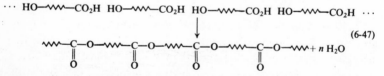

This is one way of making commercial polyesters. The other way is to esterify dihydroxyalkanes with dicarboxylic acids.

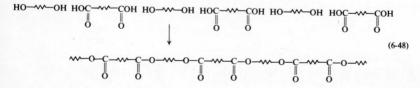

Dacron polyester fibers have this structure. If trihydroxyalkanes are used, cross-linked polymers result.

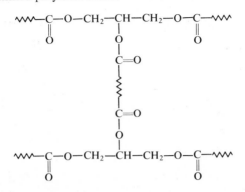

6-11 DECARBOXYLATION [1,3*d*,6,11]

The body inhales oxygen and exhales carbon dioxide. In the citric acid cycle, acetyl coenzyme A, obtained from breakdown of fats, carbohydrates, and proteins, is converted to citric acid. This acid then loses two CO_2 molecules at different stages of the cycle from CO_2H groups. The process is known as decarboxylation and has been subjected to extensive study.

$$R—\underset{\underset{|\overset{\cdot\cdot}{O}|}{\|}}{C}—\bar{O}—H \quad\longrightarrow\quad R—H + \bar{O}{=}C{=}\bar{O} \qquad (6\text{-}49)$$

Decarboxylation is particularly easy when the acid group is attached to a carbon to which other electron-withdrawing groups are attached. Ethyl acetoacetate and its mono- and dialkyl derivatives are easily converted to ketones simply by hydrolyzing the ester with dilute base, acidifying the salt and gently heating.

$$CH_3—\underset{\underset{O}{\|}}{C}—CH_2—COC_2H_5 \quad\xrightarrow[H_2O]{OH^{\ominus}}\quad CH_3—\underset{\underset{O}{\|}}{C}—CH_2—CO_2^{\ominus} \quad\xrightarrow{HA}$$

$$CH_3—\underset{\underset{O}{\|}}{C}—CH_2—\underset{\underset{O}{\|}}{C}—O—H \quad\xrightarrow{heat}\quad CH_3—\underset{\underset{O}{\|}}{C}—CH_3 + \underset{\underset{O}{\|}}{\overset{\overset{O}{\|}}{C}} \qquad (6\text{-}50)$$

Similarly

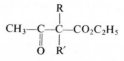

is converted to a substituted ketone

The decarboxylation of acetoacetic acid follows the rate equation

$$\text{Rate} = k[\text{CH}_3\text{COCH}_2\text{CO}_2\text{H}] + k'[\text{CH}_3\text{COCH}_2\text{CO}_2{}^\ominus]$$

The reaction involving the $\text{CH}_3\text{COCH}_2\text{CO}_2{}^\ominus$ anion goes by way of a carbanion intermediate

$$
\text{CH}_3{-}\overset{\underset{\displaystyle |\underline{\text{O}}|}{\|}}{\text{C}}{-}\text{CH}_2{-}\text{C}\overset{\displaystyle \bar{\text{O}}}{\underset{\displaystyle \underline{\text{O}}|^\ominus}{}} \longrightarrow
\left[
\begin{array}{c}
\text{CH}_3{-}\overset{\underset{\displaystyle |\underline{\text{O}}|}{\|}}{\text{C}}{-}\bar{\text{C}}\text{H}_2{}^\ominus \\[10pt]
\text{CH}_3{-}\overset{\underset{\displaystyle \underline{\text{O}}|_\ominus}{|}}{\text{C}}{=}\text{CH}_2
\end{array}
\right]^\ominus + \bar{\text{O}}{=}\text{C}{=}\bar{\text{O}}
$$

(6-51)

stabilized by charge spreading to oxygen.

The reaction involving the undissociated acid probably goes through a cyclic intermediate and forms the enol of acetone which quickly converts to the ketone.

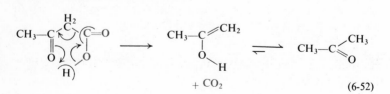

(6-52)

In both cases the ability of the keto group to accommodate extra electrons facilitates the breaking of the C—C bond.

In the decarboxylation of α-nitroisobutyric acid the rate is proportional to the concentration of the anion of the acid.

$$\overset{\bar{O}}{\underset{|\bar{O}_\ominus}{\overset{\oplus}{N}}}\!-\!\underset{CH_3}{\overset{CH_3}{\underset{|}{C}}}\!-\!\left(\overset{\bar{O}}{\underset{\bar{O}|}{C}}\right)_\ominus \xrightarrow{\text{slow}} \left[\begin{matrix}\overset{\bar{O}}{\underset{|\bar{O}_\ominus}{\overset{\oplus}{N}}}\!-\!\overset{CH_3}{\underset{CH_3}{\overset{|}{C}_\ominus}} \\ \\ \underset{|\bar{O}_\ominus}{\overset{\bar{O}_\ominus}{\overset{\oplus}{N}}}\!=\!\overset{CH_3}{\underset{CH_3}{C}}\end{matrix}\right]^\ominus + CO_2 \quad (6\text{-}53)$$

The carbanion is stabilized by charge spreading on to the NO_2 group.

If bromine is added, 2-bromo-2-nitropropane is formed without changing the rate of reaction. The rate must, therefore, be that of the decarboxylation to carbanion, the bromination being a rapid follow-up step.

$$O_2N\!-\!\overset{CH_3}{\underset{CH_3}{\overset{|}{C}_\ominus}} + \ |\bar{B}r\!\overset{\frown}{-}\!\bar{B}r| \xrightarrow{\text{rapid}} O_2N\!-\!\overset{CH_3}{\underset{CH_3}{\overset{|}{\underset{|}{C}}}}\!-\!\bar{B}r| + \ |\bar{B}r|^\ominus \quad (6\text{-}54)$$

2-Bromo-2-nitropropane

F. H. Westheimer (Harvard) and R. Steinberger have investigated the decarboxylation of dimethyloxaloacetic acid. Oxaloacetic acid,

$$O\!=\!\underset{CH_2CO_2H}{\overset{|}{C}}CO_2H$$

is decarboxylated enzymatically in the presence of manganous ion $Mn^{2\oplus}$. The dimethyl derivative

$$O\!=\!\underset{(CH_3)_2CCO_2H}{\overset{|}{C}}CO_2H$$

was studied in order to avoid complications due to carbanion formation of the type

$$O\!=\!\underset{\underset{\ominus}{CHCO_2H}}{\overset{|}{C}}\!-\!CO_2H$$

Fe^{3+}, Cu^{2+}, and Al^{3+}, when in concentrations equal to the acid, accelerate the decarboxylation by about a factor of 125, but Mn^{2+} is even more effective. The rate equation shows no participation of the undissociated acid, and a study of the effectiveness of metal ions, at varying pH, shows that the metal coordinates with the dianion, which decarboxylates to the metal-complexed enol of the final keto acid.

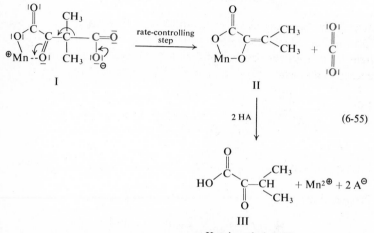

III

α-Ketoisovaleric acid

(6-55)

The complexed enol II can be detected spectrophotometrically during the reaction. The mechanism is supported by the fact that if the left-hand CO_2H group is converted to $CO_2C_2H_5$, no metal-ion catalysis is detectable nor is it if the second acid group is removed as in acetoacetic acid, $CH_3COCH_2CO_2H$.

6-12 THE INTRODUCTION AND TRANSFORMATION OF FUNCTIONAL GROUPS [9a,10]

The last section dealt with the removal of a functional group $RCO_2H \rightarrow RH + CO_2$. We will end our discussion with a survey of a common pattern for creating the CO_2H group from a hydrocarbon by the following steps:

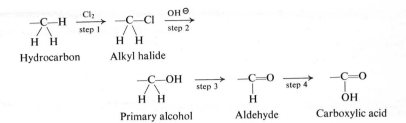

Step 2 has been discussed in detail (Sec. 2-4). It is a nucleophilic substitution. Step 1 is normally initiated by visible or ultraviolet light which supplies photons of the proper frequency and, therefore, energy to dissociate chlorine molecules into atoms.

Initiation:

$$|\overline{\text{Cl}}\text{—}\overline{\text{Cl}}| \xrightarrow{h\nu} 2 \ |\overline{\text{Cl}}\cdot$$

The subsequent reactions are a typical radical mechanism sequence.

Propagation:

$$\left. \begin{array}{l} \text{H}_3\text{C—H} + \text{Cl}\cdot \rightarrow \text{H}_3\text{C}\cdot + \text{H—Cl} \\ \text{CH}_3^{\cdot} + \text{Cl—Cl} \rightarrow \text{H}_3\text{C—Cl} + \cdot\text{Cl} \end{array} \right\}$$

Termination steps:

$$\text{H}_3\text{C}\cdot + \cdot\text{Cl} \quad \rightarrow \text{H}_3\text{C—Cl}$$
$$\text{H}_3\text{C}\cdot + \cdot\text{CH}_3 \rightarrow \text{H}_3\text{C—CH}_3$$
$$\text{Cl}\cdot + \cdot\text{Cl} \quad \rightarrow \text{Cl—Cl}$$

The fact that ethane $\text{H}_3\text{C—CH}_3$ has been detected in the chlorination of methane supports the proposed mechanism.

Energy for reaction could of course be supplied in the form of photons of the exact frequency to break particular bonds, or from heating. The relation between energy and frequency is given by the Einstein relation $E = h\nu = hc/\lambda$, where h is Planck's constant

6.63×10^{-27} erg-sec, ν is the frequency of radiation expressed as the number of waves passing a given point per second, λ is wavelength in centimeters, and c the velocity of light 3.00×10^{10} cm/sec. The velocity is of course constant for all wavelengths and is related to ν and λ by the relation $\lambda\nu = c$.

The bond dissociation energy (for cleavage to atoms) of Cl_2 is 58 kcal/mole and the corresponding wavelength in Angstrom units $(1 \text{ Å} = 10^{-8} \text{ cm})$ is given by the expression

$$E = \frac{hc}{\lambda} = \frac{6.63 \times 10^{-27} \text{ erg-sec/molecule} \times 3.00 \times 10^{-10} \text{ cm/sec}}{\lambda \text{ cm}}$$

Since Avogadro's number $= 6.02 \times 10^{23}$, and $1 \text{ erg} = 2.39 \times 10^{-11}$ kcal, 1 erg/molecule $= 2.39 \times 10^{-11} \times 6.02 \times 10^{23}$ kcal/mole. Also, $1 \text{ Å} = 10^{-8}$ cm. Therefore, the wavelength in Angstrom units

$$\lambda = \frac{hc}{E} = \frac{6.63 \times 10^{-27} \times 2.39 \times 10^{-11} \times 3.00 \times 10^{10} \times 6.02 \times 10^{23} \times 10^8}{E \text{ (kcal/mole)}}$$

$$= \frac{286,000}{E} \text{ Å}$$

Thus $286,000/58 = 4930$ Å is the wavelength needed to cleave Cl_2 molecules.

Enthalpies of reaction of the propagation steps are

$$Cl\cdot + H{-}CH_3 \rightarrow HCl + \cdot CH_3 \quad \Delta H = -1 \text{ kcal}$$

$$Cl{-}Cl + \cdot CH_3 \rightarrow Cl\cdot + Cl{-}CH_3 \quad \Delta H = -23 \text{ kcal}$$

or for the total reaction

$$Cl{-}Cl + H{-}CH_3 \rightarrow HCl + Cl{-}CH_3 \quad \Delta H = -24 \text{ kcal}$$

The 58-kcal dissociation enthalpy of Cl_2 is not part of the enthalpy of the reaction of Cl_2 and CH_4 because only a small fraction of a mole of Cl_2 needs to be dissociated to initiate the propagation steps.

For the dissociation of Cl_2 the enthalpy of dissociation is equal to the activation energy (Fig. 6-4). With a value of 58 kcal, a very

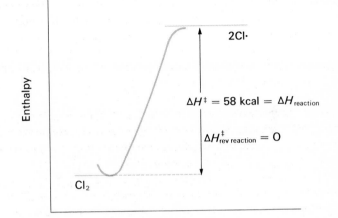

Fig. 6-4.   *Energy relations in the initiation step.*

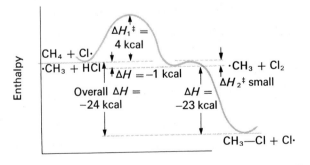

Fig. 6-5.   *Energy profile for the chlorination of methane.*

high temperature would be needed to produce an amount of dissociation equal to that produced by ultraviolet light.

Activation energies for the first propagation step is 4 kcal, and for the second it is considerably smaller giving a total reaction profile as in Fig. 6-5.

Chlorination, bromination, and iodination enthalpies are given in Table 6-5. The production of bromine and iodine atoms requires

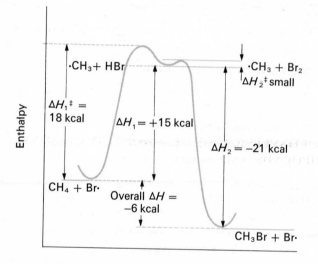

Fig. 6-6. Enthalpy profile for bromination of methane.

less energy than the dissociation of chlorine. And yet bromination of methane is much slower than chlorination while iodination is extremely slow or not detectable. The reason is found in the data in the second line. The reaction $Br\cdot + CH_4 \rightarrow HBr + \cdot CH_3$ is endothermic by 15 kcal and the activation energy must equal at least the enthalpy of an endothermic reaction. It is estimated at 18 kcal (Fig. 6-6). For the corresponding iodination reaction the activation energy is more than 31 kcal.

Table 6-5 **Enthalpies of Halogenation of Methane,** ΔH **in kcal**

		Cl	Br	I
Dissociation	$X_2 \rightarrow 2\,X\cdot$	58	46	36
Hydrogen abstraction	$X\cdot + H{-}CH_3 \rightarrow X{-}H + H_3C\cdot$	−1	15	31
Halogenation	$H_3C\cdot + X{-}X \rightarrow H_3C{-}X + X\cdot$	−23	−21	−17

Although this is a very simple photochemical (light-induced) reaction, it is a pattern for the much more complex mechanisms of reactions initiated by light, such as the bleaching of colors and photosynthesis.

6-13 CONVERSION OF ALCOHOLS TO CARBONYL COMPOUNDS AND ACIDS [7,14,15]

If we look again at the functional group sequence with which this section began

$$-CH_2{-}H \xrightarrow[\text{step 1}]{} -CH_2{-}Cl \xrightarrow[\text{step 2}]{} -CH_2{-}OH \xrightarrow[\text{step 3}]{}$$

$$-CHO \xrightarrow[\text{step 4}]{} CO_2H$$

step 1 introduces a functional group, in step 2 it is replaced by another, but steps 3 and 4 are functional group transformations, the former by removal of two hydrogen atoms, the second by the gain of an oxygen atom. We will now look at these final two steps. One of the confusing aspects is that step 4 is usually much easier than step 3 so that it is often difficult to stop a reaction at the CHO stage. This difficulty is not encountered in a decomposition process for step 3, carried out by passing the alcohol vapors through a hot tube filled with copper turnings.

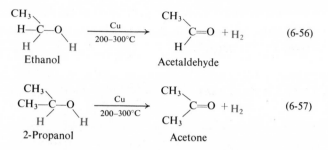

(6-56)

(6-57)

This, no doubt, is a process occurring on the copper surface, being a reversal of the hydrogenation described in Sec. 6-1.

More commonly alcohols are treated in solution with aqueous potassium permanganate, $KMnO_4$, or with chromic oxide, CrO_3, in acetic acid. Since these reagents will convert aldehydes to acids, the reactions are often carried out above the boiling point of the aldehyde (aldehydes have lower boiling points than acids because the latter hydrogen-bond in pairs and are evaporated as dimers)

$$CH_3-C\underset{O}{\overset{H}{<}}$$

Acetaldehyde
bp 20°C

$$CH_3-C\underset{O-H---O}{\overset{O---H-O}{<}}C-CH_3$$

Acetic acid dimer
bp 118°C

so that the aldehyde is distilled from the reaction mixture before it is changed to acid.

The mechanism of the chromic acid reaction of isopropyl alcohol has been worked out in detail by Westheimer, using CrO_3 with sulfuric acid in acetic acid solvent, which forms chromic acid, H_2CrO_4. The overall reaction is

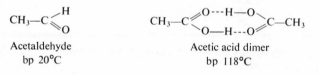

$$3\ \underset{CH_3}{\overset{CH_3}{>}}CHOH\ +\ 2\ CrO_3 + 6\ H^\oplus \longrightarrow$$

Isopropyl alcohol

$$3\ \underset{CH_3}{\overset{CH_3}{>}}C{=}O + 2\ Cr^{3\oplus} + 6\ H_2O$$

Acetone

(6-58)

Apparently, isopropyl hydrogen chromate is rapidly and reversibly formed and in the rate-determining step loses a proton from a C—H bond.

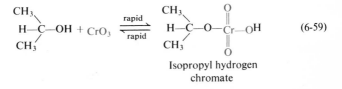

$$\text{(6-59)}$$

Isopropyl hydrogen
chromate

The isopropyl hydrogen chromate has been isolated by careful work at low temperatures. On protonation and attack by a water molecule, acting as a base, acetone is formed.

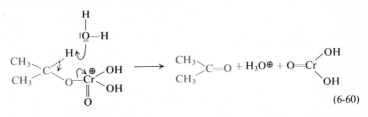

$$\text{(6-60)}$$

The H_2CrO_3 reacts rapidly in acid solution to form more CrO_3 and chromic ion $Cr^{3\oplus}$

$$3\ H_2CrO_3 + 6\ H^{\oplus} \rightarrow CrO_3 + 2\ Cr^{3\oplus} + 6\ H_2O$$

Since a C—H bond is broken in the rate-determining step, change to a C—D bond should significantly lower the rate. In support of this mechanism is the fact that $(CH_3)_2CDOH$ is converted to acetone 6.6 times more slowly than $(CH_3)_2CHOH$ at 25°C.

Chromic acid also converts aldehydes to carboxylic acids by a very similar mechanism.

Westheimer and B. Vennesland (University of Chicago) have also demonstrated the stereospecificity of the dehydrogenation of ethanol to acetaldehyde in the presence of the enzyme alcohol dehydrogenase (ADH) and the coenzyme nicotinamide-adenine nucleotide ($NAD^{\oplus}$).

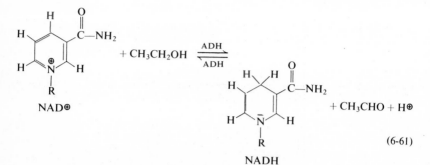

$$(6\text{-}61)$$

(R is a complex adenine phosphate sugar group).

With dideuterated ethanol, NAD⊕ takes up one deuterium atom

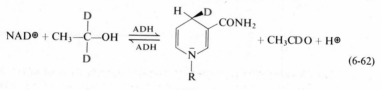

$$(6\text{-}62)$$

If the deuterated product is isolated and allowed to react with nondeuterated acetaldehyde, *only* D is lost from NADD, not the apparently equivalent H. This must imply that the enzyme can distinguish between H and D by more than their slight difference in bond strength. Furthermore, only one of the mirror-image forms of CH_3CHDOH is obtained from symmetrical acetaldehyde. Thus both the pyridine ring and the acetaldehyde molecule must be held in stereospecific positions before reaction occurs. A detailed picture of a proposed transition state has been published by Kosower (Fig. 6-7). It includes a "hydrophobic region" ("water-hating" region unable to form strong hydrogen bonds) which is supposed to prefer CH_3 to H in acetaldehyde and hence orients the aldehyde for reaction.

Aldehydes are converted to carboxylic acids even in air. Benzaldehyde, also known as oil of bitter almonds, slowly deposits a white crystalline solid, benzoic acid. The air oxidation is a radical chain process initiated by the formation of perbenzoic acid whose O—O bond cleaves into two radical fragments.

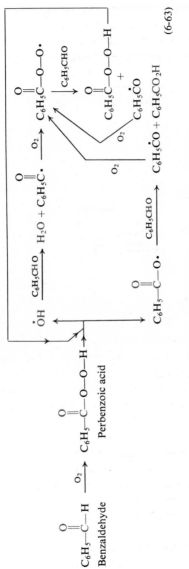

(6-63)

The overall reaction is $C_6H_5CHO + \frac{1}{2}O_2 \rightarrow C_6H_5CO_2H$.

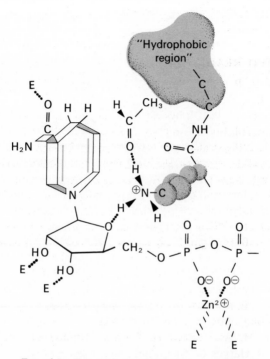

Fig. 6-7. Proposed transition state complex for reduction of acetaldehyde by NADH and ADH. [Reprinted from E. M. Kosower, "Molecular Biochemistry," p. 219, McGraw-Hill Book Company, New York, 1962, and E. M. Kosower, Biochim. and Biophys. Acta, 56: 474 (1962).] E = enzyme.

Conclusion

The study of reaction mechanisms has a long way to go before it can point in detail to the paths by which enzymes apparently effortlessly carry out their tasks. But only through the study of reaction mechanisms will enzyme mechanisms ever be elucidated. And it is clear that before the complex is understood, the simple steps and reactions of isolated functional groups should be examined. It is hoped that this book will give some glimpse into the patterns by which such studies are made.

SUGGESTED READINGS

1. Brown, B. R.: The Mechanisms of Thermal Decarboxylation, *Quart. Rev.*, **5**:131 (1951).
2. Hammett, L. P.: "Physical Organic Chemistry," chap. 11, McGraw-Hill Book Company, New York, 1940.
3. Hine, J.: "Physical Organic Chemistry," 2d ed., (*a*) chap. 10; (*b*) chap. 11; (*c*) chap. 12; (*d*) chap. 13, McGraw-Hill Book Company, New York, 1962.
4. Ihde, A.: Unravelling of Geometric Isomerism and Tautomerism, *J. Chem. Educ.*, **36**:330 (1959).
5. Ingold, C. K.: "Structure and Mechanism in Organic Chemistry," (*a*) chap. 10; (*b*) chap. 12, Cornell University Press, Ithaca, N.Y., 1953.
6. Ingraham, L. L.: "Biochemical Mechanisms," pp. 58 ff, John Wiley & Sons, Inc., New York, 1962.
7. Kosower, E. M.: "Molecular Biochemistry," sec. 2.13, McGraw-Hill Book Company, New York, 1962.
8. Mahler, H. R., and E. H. Cordes: "Biological Chemistry," chap. 10, Harper & Row, Publishers, Incorporated, New York, 1966.
9. Morrison, R. J., and R. N. Boyd: "Organic Chemistry," 2d ed., (*a*) chap. 2; (*b*) chap. 18; (*c*) chap. 27; (*d*) chap. 30; (*e*) chap. 31, Allyn & Bacon, Inc., Boston, 1966.
10. Roberts, J. D., and M. C. Caserio: "Basic Principles of Organic Chemistry," chap. 3, W. A. Benjamin Co., New York, 1964.
11. Steinberger, R., and F. H. Westheimer: Metal Ion–Catalyzed Decarboxylation: A Model for an Enzyme System, *J. Am. Chem. Soc.*, **73**:429 (1951).
12. Stewart, R.: "Oxidation Mechanisms," chap. 4, W. A. Benjamin Co., New York, 1964.
13. Sykes, P.: "A Guidebook to Mechanism in Organic Chemistry," 2d ed., chap. 7, John Wiley & Sons, Inc., New York, 1965.

14. Westheimer, F. H.: The Mechanisms of Chromic Acid Oxidations, *Chem. Rev.*, **45**:419 (1949).
15. Westheimer, F. H., and B. Vennesland in W. D. McElroy and B. Glass (eds.), "Mechanisms of Enzyme Action," p. 372, The Johns Hopkins Press, Baltimore, 1954.
16. Wheland, G. W.: "Resonance in Organic Chemistry," chap. 7, John Wiley & Sons, Inc., New York, 1955.

Index